The Case of
RUDOLF HESS

The Case of
RUDOLF HESS

A Problem in Diagnosis and Forensic Psychiatry

*By the following Physicians in the Services who
have been concerned with him from 1941 to 1946*

HENRY V. DICKS · J. GIBSON GRAHAM
M. K. JOHNSTON · D. ELLIS JONES
DOUGLAS MCG. KELLEY · N. R. PHILLIPS
G. M. GILBERT, PH.D.

Edited by J. R. REES

W · W · NORTON & COMPANY · INC · *New York*

CONTENTS

✳ NOTE BY THE AUTHORS

THE publication of what is in large measure a medical history is unusual, though not without precedent.

For obvious and very proper reasons, doctors do not normally publish accounts of their patients, alive or dead, and the fact that the patient was one by *force majeure* makes very little difference.

In this case, however, the importance of showing to as wide a public as possible the considerable abnormality of a man whose influence on world history has been marked made us, after much consideration, override the scruples which as medical men we felt.

In a world where psychopathic men can so easily become leaders and where to-day they might by their own personal whims or decisions launch another war on the nations, it is for all of us a duty to study and comprehend the nature of such men. It is important to see how morbid fantasies can activate political conduct of far-reaching importance.

It is for these reasons, after due consideration, that the material of this book has been put together and is made public.

Our decision thus taken has now been reinforced by the receipt of a letter from Rudolf Hess himself which is reproduced on the next page.

RUDOLF   HESS   NUERNBERG, DEN 27. 9. 46
NUERNBERG
GEFAENGNIS DER
SOG. KRIEGSVER-
BRECHER

HERRN
BRIGADIER DR.   R E E S
L O N D O N
- - - - - - -

        SEHR GEEHRTER HERR DR. REES,

                        HERR DR. GILBERT GAB
MIR KENNTNIS VON IHREM WUNSCH NACH EINER BESTAETIGUNG VON
MIR, WONACH ICH ES GERN SEHEN WUERDE, WENN DIE AERZTE, DIE
MICH IN ENGLAND UND SPAETER IN NUERNBERG BETREUTEN, IHRE
MICH BETREFFENDEN BERICHTE UND KRANKENGESCHICHTEN ZU WIS-
SENSCHAFTLICHEN ZWECKEN VOLL VEROEFFENTLICHEN.

        ICH TEILE IHNEN DAHER MIT, DASS ICH EINE SOLCHE VER-
OEFFENTLICHUNG SEHR BEGRUESSEN WUERDE. NICHT ABER WEIL
ICH ETWA DES GLAUBENS WAERE, DASS DADURCH DIE OEFFENT -
LICHKEIT RICHTIGER INFORMIERT WUERDE ALS BISHER, WIE HERR
DR. GILBERT MEINTE. SONDERN ICH WUERDE SIE DESHALB BEGRUES-
SEN, WEIL SIE EINMAL ALS ERGAENZENDER BEWEIS DAFUER ANGE-
SEHEN WERDEN WIRD, DASS AUF EINE BISHER NICHT BEKANNTE
WEISE MENSCHEN IN EINEN ZUSTAND VERSETZT WERDEN KOENNEN,
DER AEHNLICH DEM IST, DER DURCH EINE NACHWIRKENDE HYPNOSE
/„POSTHYPNOTHIC SUGGESTION"/ ERREICHT WERDEN KANN — EIN
ZUSTAND, IN DEM DIE BETREFFENDEN PERSONEN UNTER AUSSCHAL-
TUNG DES EIGENEN WILLENS ALLES TUN, WAS IHNEN SUGGERIERT
WURDE, VERMUTLICH OHNE DASS SIE SICH SELBST DESSEN BEWUSST
SIND.

        FUER DEN VORLIEGENDEN FALL WUERDE DER BEWEIS ERBRACHT
WERDEN, DASS SELBST EHRENHAFTE MAENNER, AERZTE UND FACH-
LEUTE VON ZUM TEIL HOHEM ANSEHEN, DURCH DEN AUSGEUEBTEN
GEISTESZWANG DAZU GEBRACHT WURDEN, SCHWERSTE VERBRECHEN
ZU BEGEHEN UND ZUGLEICH URTEILE ABZUGEBEN, DIE DER WAHR-
HEIT WIDERSPRECHEN, DAMIT DIE VERBRECHEN VERTUSCHT WERDEN.

        DIE EINZIGE BEDINGUNG FUER DAS ERTEILEN MEINES EIN -
VERSTAENDNISSES ZU DER BEABSICHTIGTEN VEROEFFENTLICHUNG
IST, DASS DIESER BRIEF MIT ABGEDRUCKT WIRD, UND ZWAR IM
VOLLEN WORTLAUT.

                        HOCHACHTUNGSVOLL

TRANSLATION

RUDOLF HESS
NUREMBERG   NUREMBERG
PRISON OF THE   27TH SEPTEMBER, 1946.
SO-CALLED
WAR CRIMINALS

BRIGADIER DR. REES
LONDON

DEAR DR. REES,

DR. GILBERT BROUGHT TO MY NOTICE YOUR WISH FOR A CONFIRMATION FROM ME THAT I SHOULD CONSIDER IT FAVOURABLY IF THE PHYSICIANS WHO HAD ME UNDER THEIR CARE IN ENGLAND AND LATER IN NUREMBERG PUBLISHED THEIR REPORTS AND CASE HISTORIES CONCERNING MYSELF FOR SCIENTIFIC PURPOSES.

I AM THEREFORE INFORMING YOU THAT I SHOULD WELCOME SUCH A PUBLICATION VERY MUCH. THIS IS NOT BECAUSE I PERHAPS HOLD THE BELIEF THAT THE PUBLIC WOULD THEREBY BE IN-FORMED MORE CORRECTLY THAN HITHERTO, AS DR. GILBERT THOUGHT. BUT I WOULD WELCOME IT BECAUSE ONE DAY IT WILL BE REGARDED AS SUPPLEMENTARY PROOF OF THE FACT THAT IN SOME HITHERTO UNKNOWN MANNER PEOPLE CAN BE PUT INTO A CONDITION WHICH RESEMBLES THAT WHICH CAN BE ATTAINED THROUGH A HYPNOSIS LEAVING ITS AFTER-EFFECTS("POST-HYPNOTIC SUGGESTION")—A CONDITION IN WHICH THE PERSONS CONCERNED DO EVERYTHING THAT HAS BEEN SUGGESTED TO THEM, UNDER THE ELIMINATION OF THEIR OWN WILL, PRESUMABLY WITHOUT THEIR BEING CONSCIOUS OF IT.

FOR THE PRESENT CASE PROOF WOULD BE SUPPLIED THAT EVEN HONOURABLE MEN, PHYSICIANS AND EXPERTS, PARTLY OF HIGH REPUTE, THROUGH THE COMPULSION EXERCISED ON THEIR MINDS, WERE BROUGHT TO COMMIT THE GRAVEST CRIMES AND AT THE SAME TIME TO DELIVER JUDGMENTS WHICH CONTRADICT THE TRUTH, IN ORDER THAT THE CRIMES SHOULD BE HUSHED UP.

THE ONLY CONDITION FOR GIVING MY CONSENT TO THE IN-TENDED PUBLICATION IS THAT THIS LETTER IS PUBLISHED WITH IT, AND THAT FULLY AND LITERALLY.

RESPECTFULLY

(sgd) RUDOLF HESS.

A*

FOREWORD BY THE EDITOR

THE story of Rudolf Hess has been something more than an interesting item of news in World War II. There have been medical and medico-legal problems of considerable importance involved, and these will be raised and re-raised, and discussed on many occasions in the future, so that it has seemed worth while to set down a fairly full record of events and observations as we have known them. It is a great relief that these circumstances and these very ordinary psychiatric findings need no longer be regarded as *Top Secret*, and can be written about with freedom.

Any medical case-history, if at all full, is bound to be somewhat repetitive, and I make no apology for the fact that this book does, despite a great deal of rigid pruning and exclusion, present a good deal of such repetition. It is in any case inevitable when a number of different observers are recording their impressions of the patient at varying times; there would in fact be something rather queer about the story if they did not give impressions which were very similar to those of their colleagues, and so it would be a mistake to cut these observations out. The ebb and flow in a case of this kind is one of the diagnostic features, and those who in reading the record find themselves bored with this must learn the art of judicious skipping.

We have tried to keep the technical concepts and terminology to a minimum in writing this record, save in Chapter XVI, where a summary of the psychopathology and a diagnosis of the condition are attempted. There is, I think, little that cannot be comprehended by the lawyer and the intelligent layman; indeed by everyone who is interested in this particular little fragment of contemporary history.

There are a number of people to whom we as a group should like to express our thanks: the responsible officers and men who have so patiently guarded and cared for Hess during these years, the Intelligence officers who at the beginning did so much to help our understanding of him, and perhaps above all to

Sgt. Everett, R.A.M.C., and his colleagues who formed the very efficient and patient band of mental nurses caring for the Deputy Fuehrer for four years. Dr. John Rickman, Dr. George Riddoch, and Mr. John Dickson Carr have all spent much time and thought in helping to improve the book.

Finally we acknowledge with gratitude the co-operation and help of those concerned at the Foreign Office and the War Office (Directorate of Prisoners of War), who also have read and passed the manuscript, and also of the War Crimes Commissions of the United States and of Great Britain.

J. R. REES

London.

THE CASE OF RUDOLF HESS

THE dramatic admission by Hess that he had been fooling the Court at Nuremberg has raised a nice question of psychiatric diagnosis which, in its legal implications, is far from academic. On the face of it his admission suggests that he has been malingering; but the psychiatrists have said that he has a hysterical amnesia, and it has been reported that during his imprisonment in England he showed delusions of persecution and made two desperate attempts at suicide. Also he had been hallucinated. It is certainly not possible to maintain that all his abnormalities have been simulated wilfully. Whether he malingered his recent loss of memory or not, the suicidal attempts were out of keeping with any such explanation of his conduct, and comparisons with the well-planned attempt at hanging himself made by the author of the *Road to Endor* would hardly be applicable.

That Hess is entirely a hysteric is very unlikely. Apart from the psychotic symptoms he has exhibited, his previous personality was not in keeping with such a view, nor his strong and quasi-mystical feeling that he had a mission. His amnesia could, of course, quite well be of the hysterical type without the whole illness being a hysterical one.

The main probable diagnosis would appear to be paranoid schizophrenia. The difficulties that arise in accepting this view turn on the concurrence of hysterial amnesia and the subsequent self-accusation that he had only pretended to have forgotten. But hysterical symptoms are by no means uncommon in schizophrenia; a psychogenic disturbance of memory is well attested in this condition and could furthermore be apparently produced by a negativistic taciturnity expressing itself in abrupt statements such as "I cannot remember". Hess's reported demeanour at the trial betokened an aversion and indifference of the type fairly common in autistic schizophrenics. Moreover, the hysteriform disturbances seen in persons who are in prison are often difficult to distinguish from schizophrenia, and have often turned out to be the prelude to indubitable and hopeless schizophrenic disorder.

But speculation about the nature of Hess's disorder must clearly wait upon the detailed report of the finding made by the various psychiatrists who have examined him since he first arrived in England, and particularly upon the setting within which his present symptoms—and especially his mocking assertion that he has only pretended not to remember—must be judged.

CHAPTER I

THE PARACHUTIST

At the beginning of May, 1941, Great Britain and Germany had been at war for twenty months, and life in the United Kingdom could hardly be called dull. On April 26th, a few days before this story begins, Athens had fallen to the German Army. Although we did not know it, a few weeks later, on June 22nd, Russia was to be invaded by the German Army, and had this been known, it might have thrown light on some of the other events that took place, notably on the particular episode with which this book is concerned. On May 10th, 1941, London had its heaviest night raid of the war by the Luftwaffe, and in that raid Germany lost thirty-three aircraft over London; that was in itself a considerable happening. It almost seemed as though there was some connection between the two occurrences when we heard a day or so later that on the same day, May 10th, there had baled out and parachuted to earth in the South of Scotland a pilot of a Messerschmitt who eventually turned out to be Rudolf Hess.

Dressed in the uniform of a hauptmann (flight-lieutenant) of the Luftwaffe, he at first announced his name as "Horn", but his identity was fairly quickly recognised and it was realised that he had arrived where he did because he was hoping to land on the Duke of Hamilton's estate in order to contact him.

Under these circumstances and at this stage of the war, it was something more than a nine days' wonder that Hitler's deputy, who was leader of the Nazi Party, the Reich Minister without Portfolio, a member of the Ministerial Council for the Defence of the Reich, and a member of the Secret Cabinet Council of Germany, should have arrived unannounced and without any pre-arranged contacts in this country, on what appeared to be an exceedingly vague mission.

If this country was somewhat surprised, his own country was even more astonished. Rudolf Hess had been constantly in the public eye in his special position as Hitler's close personal friend and supporter, and a few days previously on May Day he had

I

spoken in public. No one knew of any serious disagreement at that moment in the group of Nazi leaders, so that inside Germany at any rate there was nothing to justify the idea which originated in Great Britain and America that Hess had taken flight to escape some personal threat to his life. The German people were not told of the flight until May 13th, when the newspapers all produced the same headlines "Rudolf Hess meets with accident" and the same story:

"Party Member Hess, because of an illness of many years' standing which was becoming worse, and who had been forbidden by the Fuehrer to do any flying, went against this order and obtained an aeroplane on Saturday, May 10th. At 6.0 he left Augsberg in the plane and has not been heard from since. A letter which he left behind shows from its confused writing the unfortunate traces of mental derangment and it is feared that Party Member Hess has sacrificed himself to a fixed idea. It is felt that somewhere on this trip he has crashed and probably perished. The Fuehrer has ordered the immediate arrest of Hess's adjutants, who alone knew of the flight and of the fact that such flights had been forbidden by the Fuehrer."

There was, we are told, considerable confusion and excitement both official and private in Germany, and many statements were reproduced in the foreign Press. Hitler declared that Hess in his mental illness had consulted astrologers and healers instead of orthodox and recognised physicians. After a conference of Party Leaders and Gauleiters, the Press were taken into session and the spokesman at this conference said that Hess had suffered from stomach ailments and that for some time his work had been done for him by his chief assistant, Bormann. This same spokesman also said that Hess suffered from the "hallucination" that he could bring about peace by sacrificing himself. A day or two later came a further statement:

"As far as it is possible to tell from papers left behind by Party Member Hess it seemed that he lived in a state of hallucination as a result of which he felt he could bring about an understanding between England and Germany. It is a fact that Hess, according to a report from London, jumped from his aeroplane near the town to which he was trying to go and was found there injured. The National Socialist

Party regrets that this idealist fell as a victim to his hallucinations. This however will have no effect on the continuation of the war which has been forced upon Germany. Dr. Karl Haushofer, head of the Geo-political Institute, Willi Messerschmitt, Frau Hess, and others were arrested."

We were told at the time by American correspondents in Berlin that it was thought that Hess had gone to Britain to suggest a joint war against Russia. They also reported the idea that the plan to call Hess insane had originated with Hitler himself.

Not unnaturally the German people faced by this announcement of Hess's insanity wondered why, if he had been insane all this time, he had been permitted to continue as Hitler's deputy, and probably to some of them the same thought occurred that naturally came to our minds in this country and in America: if Hess was of unsound mind and still carrying on, what about the rest of the Nazi leaders?

The arrival of Hess was exciting and it was also potentially important as an unusual event in the history of the war, but it was also a small additional embarrassment to the British Government. The material content of the investigations and interrogations of Hess as to his purpose and mission in coming here are not the primary concern of this book. They were somewhat arid, if one can judge from the reports of Lord Simon's interview with him quoted at the Nuremberg trial and referred to in a later chapter. The problems which faced the authorities in this country were to keep Hess safe from escape and safe from himself, and the further problem of security which had to be tackled was to ensure his safety from attack by other people who might possibly have formed their own conclusions about him and wish to take the law into their own hands as to his future. Our self-appointed prisoner was therefore something of a responsibility from many angles.

As Chapter III will show, Hess had suffered some minor injuries in his parachute drop, and consequently was admitted to the Military Hospital at Drymen at the southern point of Loch Lomond for a few days, where careful investigations were made and such treatment as was necessary was started. After a few days it was decided that pending the provision of suitable accommodation for him he should be moved to the Tower of

London. From there, as soon as the necessary arrangements had been carried through, he was taken down to Mytchett Place near Aldershot, where he arrived in the third week of his captivity. By this time it was clear that there were evidences of mental disturbance which made the problem of his care a medical matter as well as one of security, and these two factors had to be taken into account throughout the whole of his four and a half years in Great Britain.

For reasons that will be easily understood, great care was taken to keep as secret as possible all the arrangements that were being made for Hess, and his whereabouts was not disclosed at any time, though later on there were a few leakages of information. Though many people knew of his whereabouts in this country, the necessary secrecy was very well maintained. At Mytchett Place a considerable guard was maintained, and in order to avoid wasting the time of the necessary personnel, the garden was turned into a defence strong-point, and it was used as a training ground for troops from a neighbouring camp, who were periodically changed. From time to time newspaper comment and Parliamentary questions would raise the issue of what was happening to Hess and it was assumed that he was fed much better than the average Britisher, that he had all kinds of special privileges, etc. In fact there was no basis for any of these ideas. As an unusual type of prisoner he was treated differently from other German prisoners of war in that he was kept by himself, and in consequence had a bedroom and a sitting-room throughout his stay. As a solitary person he had more contact with his guard than he would have had in a prison camp, and, largely for medical reasons, officers of the guard would from time to time have meals with him. He ate the same "ration" food that they did, and he was at all times under surveillance and rigid restrictions. As time wore on he was allowed to have things which were at first denied him, i.e. he was able to listen to the wireless, and to read English papers and selected English and German books. He was visited by representatives of the Swiss Government, the protecting power, as other prisoners of war were visited. He was allowed to write brief letters home after some time, which of course passed through censorship as did the letters of all other German prisoners in this country. He had the same limited amount of money given to him, out of which civilian clothes were bought for him, and renewals were made when necessary. At a later stage, when he was in Wales, for reasons of health he was taken out, with a guard, in a car so that he could walk more freely and be unobserved in the country, though very strict limitations were placed on the number of such short expeditions.

The army physician who looked after him at Drymen (Lt.-Col. Gibson Graham) came south with him and handed over at the end of May to a psychiatrist, Major Dicks, who later was replaced at Mytchett by Capt. Johnston. A psychiatrist, who also acted as medical officer to the guard, was resident or on the spot the whole time from then onwards, and Major Ellis Jones finally flew with him in October, 1945 to Nuremberg and handed him over to the American Army authorities, and to the medical care of Major Douglas Kelley, U.S.M.C., psychiatrist to the prison at Nuremberg. From the time of the attempt at suicide made by Hess at Mytchett, six trained mental nurses (mental nursing orderlies of the Royal Army Medical Corps) were in attendance so that he was never left without trained supervision, two of them being on for each shift of eight hours.

In June, 1942 for various reasons Hess was moved from Mytchett to Maindiff Court, Abergavenny, in South Wales. Mytchett Place was somewhat noisy; it was a large house which was wasteful from the point of view of the size of the guard needed, and the new arrangement was realised to be more economical. Maindiff Court Hospital had been built just before the war as an admission hospital for the Monmouthshire County Mental Hospital, a mile and a half away. It had not been used for the treatment of psychiatric patients, since the war had come and it was turned over to the purpose of an ordinary general hospital for the Ministry of Health, taking sick and convalescent officers and other ranks from the Services. One wing of this one-storey building proved extremely suitable for Hess, who had two small adjacent rooms with a veranda outside leading on to an airing court with high railings around it. Here he spent the rest of his time until October, 1945. The guard could be reduced to much smaller numbers, and Major Ellis Jones, a very experienced psychiatrist, was already in charge of all the general medical work of Maindiff Court Hospital and so was on the spot. An additional advantage was that Dr. Phillips, the medical superintendent of the Mental Hospital, was constantly in and out of Maindiff Court and so was available for consultation and for relief for Major Ellis Jones. This "Prisoner of War Reception Station", established specifically for this particular patient, was therefore a very successful and relatively economical arrangement. While he was at Maindiff Court, Abergavenny, the only small leakages of information in the Press occurred. From time to time public interest would surge up, starting perhaps in America or sometimes in this country, and Press representatives would attempt to get some information and even to get long-distance photographs of the hospital grounds and of the prisoner. This was quite understandable, but in fact very little of any importance leaked out in this way.

It is perhaps not quite clear to some readers why so much care had to be taken to secure the bodily and mental state of Hess. A little consideration will make it obvious however that had any harm come to him, either from outside or at his own hands, there would have been serious risk that this would have been attributed to a deliberate policy of the British Government, and would have had its repercussions on Allied prisoners in German hands. Hess himself was quite well aware of this and on a number of occasions remarked quite cheerfully about what would be thought if he himself were to die in England.

This is, then, a very brief factual statement about Hess's arrival and about his places and method of residence in Great Britain. By the time he arrived at Nuremberg on October 6th, 1945, the war was over and he became one of a considerable group in the city prison, and from then on he lived in a prison cell alongside his late colleagues.

The chapters which follow set out in brief some of the facts and impressions about his medical state as seen by various observers. What was Hess like? Was Hess mad? What was wrong with him? These were the sort of problems that naturally were being asked and that we asked ourselves. This book will at least provide some of the material from which any reader may draw his own conclusions.

CHAPTER II

THE EARLIER HISTORY OF RUDOLF HESS

THE doctor whose help is sought by patients in the ordinary course of his professional work has very little difficulty in taking a full history. The psychiatrist naturally wishes to know a good deal about the background of his patient, the family history, the stresses of childhood and adolescence, and the educational and occupational history as well as the details of ill health that may have come about at any period of a patient's life.

During the years in which Hess was under observation in Great Britain it was peculiarly frustrating to each of us who tried to take a full history, as we did on a number of occasions, that we always came up against a suspicious attitude and a refusal to communicate the facts of his past life in any adequate way. Perhaps it was natural, despite the many complaints of sickness and ill health, and still more signs of abnormality, which latter he didn't recognise, that he regarded himself as a prisoner, a very important prisoner too. Almost till the end he believed fully, so far as we could see, that the tables would be turned by a German victory.

Fortunately we knew something of his background from the public Press in the years preceding the outbreak of war, and we had some slight extra insight into his history because, curiously enough, the brother of Rudolf Hess had been well known to a relative of one of the collaborators in this book. From time to time a certain number of facts emerged either in casual conversation or as the result of indirect questioning, and these when put together constitute a fairly clear and informative picture of the patient's background. It has been possible to add to this and to fill in some details from the official historical record made at Nuremberg, where the whole situation was different and it was easier to get the material. In addition some of the comments made by Rudolf Hess's late secretary have been of value. The historical sketch which follows is therefore composed from these various sources.

Rudolf Hess was born in Egypt, at Alexandria, on April 26th, 1896. He was therefore just forty-five when he left Germany and flew to this country. His grandfather had emigrated from Germany to Egypt and established a business as a wholesale merchant, which Hess's father took over. Fritz Hess, the father of our subject, had married Klara Muench, who came from Hof in Bavaria. Hess's mother is (in 1946) still alive. There were four children, the brother Alfred, who is still alive and is an accountant in industry, and two sisters, one of whom married an operatic singer and the other married a colonel in the German Army.

On one occasion, when the question of the sterilisation of the unfit and its relation to family history was under discussion, Hess was asked: "Surely your family would have someone with epilepsy, or someone who was certified?" but he denied this. It since appears however to be the case that one of his mother's brothers had committed suicide in uncertain circumstances and that his father's sister had been in a mental hospital and had died early, probably while mentally disturbed. About this aunt and her breakdown, Hess is reported to have remarked to his secretary that he thought it was the result of his grandfather having been drunk at the time of conception. This child had been born long after the other children and possibly because of the stimulus of alcohol.

As one finds so often in a family history of this period, Hess's father was very strict in the early days, though in later life he became materially altered and gentler in his approach. (He died in 1941.) It is said that Hess and his brother and sisters only dared to play at all cheerfully when the father had gone out to business.

For six years Rudolf Hess attended the German school in Alexandria and at the age of twelve was sent to Germany as a boarder in the Evangelisches Paedagogium at Godesberg am Rhein, where he remained for three years. We are told that he was popular both in his first school in Alexandria and at Godesberg. The teachers found him an attentive and earnest pupil and liked him. Feeling that he had been brought up as an exile from the Fatherland, he was intensely patriotic during his boarding-school career. The history master here had a very marked influence on him, and later this master was given a fairly prominent position in the National Socialist Party to guide the teaching of history.

Hess would have liked to study science and mathematics, but his father's intention was to make him a merchant, and in consequence we find him at fifteen leaving public school and going to the Ecole Superieure de Commerce at Neufchatel, Switzerland. After a year there, he went in 1912 to Hamburg and served a commercial apprenticeship. The World War broke out in 1914 and Rudolf Hess volunteered with alacrity and joined the 1st Bavarian Infantry Regiment. He was delighted to get away from the commercial job, which he disliked. He fought on the Western Front and was wounded twice, in 1916, and again in 1917, when he had a gunshot wound of the chest which injured his lung. After this he was commissioned and made a lieutenant, and in 1918 transferred to the Air Corps, where he was most assiduous in his training, and is said to have become an efficient pilot. This certainly would seem to have been borne out by his later experience so recently as 1941. His training occupied so much of 1918 that in fact the war was over before he was able to take any further active part. He only got back to active operations in October, 1918, just before the Armistice.

At the end of 1918 Hess was in Munich, where he joined a nationalist and anti-Semitic group. He took part in the fight against the Left wing government of Bavaria and was wounded in the leg in a fight against the social democrats in May, 1919. In 1920 Rudolf Hess came to what was clearly a vital point in his career. Up to this time he had been enthusiastic and patriotic and had enjoyed many aspects of the war and had also been drawn into Right wing gang activities. He now enrolled as a student at Munich University, taking history, economics, and geopolitics (he never graduated). This brought him under the influence of Professor Karl Haushofer, whose influence from this time on was to dominate much of his philosophy and his thought, and eventually, as we shall see, was to be responsible for his flight to Scotland. Hess is said to have joined the embryonic National Socialist Party in June, 1920, though from his own story the link with Hitler was not made until 1923. In 1921 Hess was responsible in Munich for provoking a brawl of his party with the social democrats and as the result of this himself suffered a head injury of no great severity. Nevertheless, this was his fourth injury, two in the war, and two resulting

from brawls. As a result of this Munich brawl the Nazi Storm
Troops began to be organised, and Hess became one of their
active leaders, organising a special student battalion. We know
very little in any authoritative way about his state of mind or his
psychological development at this time, but he told us that in
1923 he heard Hitler speaking in one of the beer cellars in
Munich, was immediately greatly attracted to him, and told his
fiancée that he thought this man would ultimately save Germany. This certainly was a turning-point in his life, and from
now onwards the whole of his energies were devoted to the
advancement of the National Socialist movement. The complicated history of his activities from this time is for the most
part not relevant to the understanding of the man's character
and mental state. Rumour has it that during one of the
frequent brawls he shielded Hitler from the blow of a bottle
which landed on Hess's head. From the Putsch of November,
1923, he moved from one exciting intrigue to another. After the
failure to overthrow the Bavarian Government, he escaped
across the mountains to Austria, returning soon afterwards, and
served seven and a half months of his eighteen months' sentence
of imprisonment in the Landsberg fortress with Hitler. Here he
acted as Hitler's secretary, and Hitler dictated parts of *Mein
Kampf* to him during this time. Hess himself regards this as a
definite collaboration and it seems probable that as a student of
Karl Haushofer some of the ideas and concepts that he had
acquired of geopolitics found their way into the writing of the
Nazi bible.

In 1924 Hess returned to the German Academy in Munich,
where for a while he was an assistant to Haushofer. After this
he became secretary and personal adjutant to Hitler, and he
remained as such until 1933, winning Hitler's complete
confidence and ensuring his own future position. He wrote
many of the propaganda pamphlets that were put out during
that period, and was in on all the planning.

In 1932 Gregor Strasser broke away from Hitler, and the
latter organised at that time the central political commission
which was to crush all opposition, and put Rudolf Hess in
charge of this organisation. From this time on, therefore, he had
in his hands the main supervision of the political development
of the Party throughout Germany. From then on we find him

organising a series of groups and organisations all of which strengthened the hand of the Party and suppressed freedom of thought and liberty throughout the country. All the universities, schools, and religious societies came under the domination of Hess. He authorised the establishment of the German labour front, and later in 1935 signed the anti-Jewish legislation which played so large a part in the activities of the Party in Germany.

By virtue of his position, Hess had power to decide about the qualification for membership of the Nazi Party, and at all the Party Congresses it was he who administered the oath of allegiance. There is no doubt that in this way and through his representing Hitler on all manner of public occasions he came to be regarded as the man most linked with the Party objectives and organisation. In 1934 it is said that Hess played an important part in the Roehm purge, and he was probably personally one of the main executioners. While in this country, when he talked about Captain Roehm his manner and feeling seemed to indicate such a degree of hatred that it suggested the repression of homosexual trends in himself, a matter which may be of some importance but which it was never possible fully to investigate.

In 1935 Hitler decided that Hess should participate in the legislation of all departments of the government in addition to concerning himself with Party matters, and from then on he took part in the preparation of all decrees of the Fuehrer. He became a member of the Secret Cabinet Council in 1938 which was planning the policies of foreign aggression. It is said that he was responsible for devising the scheme whereby Nazi agents disguised as Austrian patriots were to assassinate Von Papen, then German Ambassador to Austria. Hess's plan was discovered, so that this never materialised. Finally at the outbreak of the war he was a member of the Ministerial Council for the Defence of the Reich, a body with six members, in whom was concentrated all supreme legislative and executive power.

This is but a shortened list of the many political and public activities of Rudolf Hess in the years preceding the war, but it serves to indicate the influence that he had and the trust that was reposed in him in the Party, immediately preceding his flight to Scotland. This vivid and exciting career came to an end on May 10th, 1941, and even had Hess been until that time a completely stable and well-balanced man, the contrast between May 9th and all that followed after May 10th of that year would have been sufficient to create a major psychological stress.

Having put together some of the factual history of Hess as we know it, it is disappointing to have to admit that we have very little accurate information about his previous medical history. We know that he was wounded twice in the 1914-18 war, that he had at least two wounds in brawls in the early days of the Nazi Party. He stated when in England that he had at various times suffered from trouble with his gall bladder, from renal trouble, from colitis, and also from a pain in the region of the heart. The fact that he was a teetotaller and non-smoker, coupled with his general personality make-up, may suggest that the old cardiac pains before he came to this country were symptoms of effort syndrome. In 1937 he had had a prostatitis, but the nature of this is unknown. On his arrival in this country the Kahn test for syphilis was negative. We know from the history given by him, and it was confirmed by his late secretary, that he had since 1933 at any rate had attacks of abdominal pains. She also said that he was not very good at climbing up steep slopes "on account of the wound in his lung". There was no evidence of any such difficulty during his time in Great Britain. He had also had from time to time since 1933 attacks which were said to be due to his gall bladder. We know that he had consulted numerous doctors, running from one to the other and never having the patience to let any one physician carry out treatment. Recently, particularly since 1938, he had turned more and more to unorthodox practitioners, those practising nature-cure, irido-diagnosis, and chiropraxy. His secretary related that the Fuehrer had ridiculed Hess for his running around to all sorts of doctors and quacks. This account of his growing hypochrondria and concern for his health is borne out by the fact that on his arrival in Scotland his pockets were stuffed with homeopathic and nature-cure medicines, and his account of the dietetic restrictions that he had placed upon himself provided further confirmation. He excluded eggs, jams and dried foods, and drank only very weak tea.

Hess's mother is said to have had a marked interest in nature-cure and semi-medical matters, in contrast to his father, who in his later years had grown away from being the rather dour, stern man that he was when Hess was a boy, and had become a normal cheerful old gentleman who liked plenty of amusement. Part of the interest which Hess displayed in the various medical interests was, we believe, caused by a fear of cancer. He was dissatisfied that no cure for cancer had been found, and felt that possibly through unorthodox practice some solution of the problem could be found. Further he had a constant drive to greater efficiency, feeling that if he was tired something must be wrong with him. This may possibly link on to old fears of the consequences of adolescent auto-erotic sexual practices, to which Goering referred in a somewhat shamefaced way when asked about Hess by the doctors at Nuremberg. It would seem that Hess's interest in horoscopes and the semi-occult, which has been spoken of in the Press, began about the beginning of the war. He placed great emphasis on the influence of the stars and on the diagrams worked out for him by an elderly woman fortune-teller. His actual flight to Scotland may have been influenced by this, though he told us that in fact the main deciding factor in bringing him on this flight from Germany was that Professor Haushofer had dreamed of him flying across the ocean.

We have certain other impressions of Hess as a personality which are derived partly from disconnected remarks made by him and partly from matters related by his secretary, but none of them very accurately confirmed by Hess himself. Hess had been engaged for several years before he married Ilse Proehl of Hanover in 1927. During all his time in this country he showed little interest in his wife, and when her letters failed to come to him, he would not bother to write to her. We are told that after marriage he would neither allow portraits of his wife to be published in any magazine in Germany, nor would he allow her to take any place in the Party or the women's organisations attached to it. She never appeared in public except at a concert or theatre. He was always extremely attached to his son, who was born ten years later, in 1937.

The humanitarian feelings for women and children who were being bombed in Great Britain which influenced him partly in making his journey are not without significance when one thinks of the side of his character other than the ruthlessness which has been so evidently displayed. There are stories confirmatory of this, as for example one occasion which his secretary relates when they were having tea in the garden and some wasps had got caught in the honey jar; Hess picked them out with his spoon, washed them carefully, and put them into the sun to dry. He earned a reputation for kindliness to subordinates and those who worked with him, and both his ex-secretaries who were interviewed at Nuremberg had evidently got the warmest feelings of personal regard for him. One of his secretaries said "he was so kind and so noble that one felt obliged to be the same way as much as possible and to do for him as much as one could; none of us minded working with him till far after midnight. I remember one occasion when he came home very late so that the supper had to be warmed again and again, and Frau Hess was reproachful and said it was too much trouble for the cook and the maidservant to stay up so late; afterwards the maid came to me and said, please do tell him that we are quite willing to work for him at any time, day or night; we never mind that, we are glad to do something for him; that was significant of the opinion of the people who had to deal with him personally."

It should be noted that this form of hero-worship of a great man by his female secretary and by his lady cook, in the emotional atmosphere prevailing in Germany at the time of these events, is perhaps hardly evidence as to character.

CHAPTER III

IT will be of interest to record the very earliest medical observations that were made on Rudolf Hess after that landing in Scotland near the Duke of Hamilton's estate. The following details are written by Dr. Graham, who was then Lt.-Col., R.A.M.C., and Officer in Charge of the Medical Division at Drymen Military Hospital, on the Duke of Roxburghe's estate near Glasgow.

"Rudolf Hess was admitted to the Military Hospital, Drymen, Glasgow, on May 11th, 1941. He said he was Alfred Horn, age forty-six years, a hauptman in the Luftwaffe, and had landed the previous evening by parachute from an aeroplane, piloted by himself.

"Unaware of his identity, I visited him the next day. He complained of feeling confused, especially after talking for any length of time, and ascribed this to the strain which he had undergone. He mentioned that he had lost consciousness before landing by parachute (there was no history of bleeding from ears or nose), and complained of pain over the 12th dorsal vertebra and right ankle. X-ray films showed a small chip fracture of the spinous process of 12 D. vertebra, and a small fragment of bone separated from the anterior surface of the tibia at the right ankle joint.

"On May 13th, learning for the first time his identity, I again saw him. He looked well, and while guarded in his conversation, did not strike me as being mentally of unsound mind. He told me he had come to this country on a special mission, the nature of which I would learn in due course. He spoke rationally, but obviously regarded himself as an important personage, and was not prepared to talk intimately with strangers. Physical examination did not reveal any evidence of organic disease. B.P. 130/85. Urine: no albumen, no glucose, no abnormal deposit The Kahn Test (blood) was negative, and an X-ray of the chest showed clear lung fields, save for a small calcified area in the upper right zone.

"Hess remained at Drymen until *May* 16*th*, when he was removed to the Tower of London. During this period he showed himself to be a man very nervous and introspective about his health. He mentioned he had consulted a variety of doctors, mainly homeopaths. His chief physicians were Dr. Kurt Schauer, Hollreigelskreut Homeopathic Hospital, Munich, and Herr Reutter, Hohenzollern Strasse, Munich. He had been treated for cholecystitis, colitis and kidney trouble. He flew to this country with his pockets filled with various drugs, chiefly homeopathic, including an elixir brought by Dr. Sven Hedin, the Swedish explorer, from a Thibetan Lamasery, which he had been told was a specific cure for gall bladder troubles. He had also a collection of vitamin preparations, glucose and sedatives.* His only other possessions were a considerable number of photographs of his son, his wife appearing in one as a subsidiary figure handing the child a book.

"On *May* 16*th*, arrangements were made for Hess to be removed to London by the night train. He took an interest in the journey by ambulance, and seemed to enjoy his central position in an important security move, but during the actual train journey he became extremely difficult. He objected to the presence of an officer guard in his compartment, and said he could not sleep if eyes watched him throughout the night. He demanded to be left in complete darkness. When these requests were refused he became violent, and later sulky, and would take only a small quantity of sedative provided for him.

"Hess remained in the Tower of London from *May* 17*th* to *May* 21*st*, and during this period behaved rationally. He stated he felt better, talked little about his ailments, and was able to

---

* The Medical Research Council reporting on these various drugs on May 29th, 1941, wrote:
"It seems quite clear from the remarkable collection of drugs that Captain H. was intent on protecting himself against all assault of the devil so far as his flesh was concerned, and, if he knew the action of all the drugs he carried, he has obviously missed his vocation and ought to have made a very handy general practitioner. He seems to have protected himself (1) against the pains of injury by opium alkaloids; (2) against the discomfort of headaches by aspirin, etc.; (3) against the pains of colic by atropin; (4) against the fatigue of flying by pervitin; (5) against the sleeplessness following pervitin by barbiturates; (6) against constipation by a saline mixture, and against every other ailment to which flesh is heir by mixtures of unknown products made up along homeopathic lines, i.e. so dilute that it is impossible to say what they are. This reliance upon allopathy for real bodily ailments and his further belief in homeopathy for other discomforts seem to represent a curious outlook on medical science."

walk about his room, although with a slight limp. There was one incident on the 18*th*. He was making notes, and asked to speak to the Duke of Hamilton and Mr. Ivone Kirkpatrick. On being told that his request was noted, but could not be immediately carried out, he became offended and sulky.

[On *May 19th, 1941* Hess wrote a letter to Germany in which he toyed with the idea that his death was being encompassed, and that it would be misrepresented as suicide. This however would bear fruit in bringing peace and also in bringing revenge on the British war-mongers.—*Ed.*]

"On arrival on *May 21st* at the quarters set aside for his reception at Mytchett, he became very agitated, and inquired about the reason for a wire fence round the house and wire grilles outside his windows and quarters. He was restless, ate little, and wrote a letter to the Duke of Hamilton, which he later recalled and re-wrote.

"He was extremely agitated next day, and told me he was convinced he was surrounded by Secret Service agents who would accomplish his death either by driving him to commit suicide, committing a murder staged to look like suicide, or by administering poison in his food. I was unable to convince him of the groundlessness of such assertions, but his suspicions kept shifting to various persons. At the beginning of his stay it was focused on officers in immediate attendance on him, but later was transferred to officers and men of the guard. He remained intensely suspicious of food during my attendance; even when he dined with us, and the food was served from a common dish, he would select carefully, say a chop, but never the one which happened to be nearest him.

"After a few days at Mytchett, he briefly recounted his life history. He described how he had been brought up in Alexandria and had fought in the Great War, and had been a hauptman in the Luftwaffe. (This was the reason for his appearing as Hauptman Alfred Horn.) He said that for the purpose of his present mission he could not take a higher rank than he held in the last war. He appeared to think the assumption of the name Alfred Horn and the year's difference in age between Hess and Horn a master-stroke of cunning. In 1918, appalled at the plight of Germany, he determined to work for the betterment of his stricken Fatherland, and not to return to his father's business in Alexandria.

"He went to Munich to study under his old friend, Professor Karl Haushofer, and attended lectures in 'geopolitik'. Hess had great faith in Haushofer, whom he considered possessed the gift of second sight. He recounted that during the Great War (1914-18) Haushofer, then a general, often refused to allow himself and staff to travel by a certain train because he had a premonition that it would be bombed by the Royal Flying Corps, 'and,' concluded Hess, 'he was always right.'

"During his stay in Munich he attended a meeting, and was hypnotised by the presence and fire of the speaker. He made enquiries, and discovered that the orator was a man called Adolph Hitler, who had founded a party called the National Socialist Party, which at that time consisted of between thirty to forty members. As he described this incident, Hess became enthusiastic. He said: 'It came over me, as if in a vision, that this man would lead Germany to greatness, so I joined the Party, and who would have thought then that that Party would now be Germany?'

"Hess was never tired of talking of his Fuehrer, whom he regarded as a God, and delighted in recounting stories, e.g., the construction of the autobahns, the writing of *Mein Kampf*, in which his hero was the central figure.

"Hess maintained that Hitler had no designs against Britain or the Empire, but was determined that Germany would be the dominant power in Europe, must regain her colonies and such ones from France as she required. Thus, Hess affirmed, he became depressed at the thought of needless slaughter on both sides, since, in his opinion, nothing could prevent Germany from winning the war against Britain. He said he was horrified at the heavy air-raids on London in 1940, and loathed the thought of killing young children and their mothers. This feeling was intensified when he saw his own wife and son and led to the idea of flying to Britain and arranging peace with the large anti-war faction which he thought existed in this country. He stressed that personal advantage played no part in this scheme—it was an increasing idealistic urge.

It was with such thoughts in his mind that he was impressed on hearing his prophet Haushofer express similar sentiments, and mention the Duke of Hamilton as a person of common sense, who must be horrified at this senseless slaughter. Haushofer also remarked that he had seen Hess on three occasions in a dream piloting an aeroplane he knew not where. Hess took these remarks, coming from such a man, as a message to fly to this country as an emissary of peace, to seek the Duke of Hamilton, who would conduct him to King George. The British Government would be thrown out of office and a party desiring peace installed in its place. He was insistent that he would have no dealings with that 'clique' who would do all in their power to thwart him, but he was very vague as to what statesmen would replace them, and seemed to be extremely ill-informed as to the names and standing of our politicians. It is also of interest to note that Hess knew nothing of the Duke of Hamilton beyond having met him at a dinner in Berlin when the Olympic Games were held there.

"From such cloudy material Hess worked out his plan of flying to this country, seeking out the Duke of Hamilton and then King George, with his own peace proposals to lay before a new government. He described how he approached Willi Messerschmidt and obtained facilities for long-distance flying inside Germany in training for the event, and when he was prepared, he set out on his voyage. He maintained that there were no confederates and that he showed considerable skill in arranging his journey, working out the route himself, and with an accuracy which enabled him to land only some ten miles from his destination, Dungavel.

"These conversations, with their mixture of grandiose background and flimsy, woolly substance, convinced me of the need of a psychiatrist's opinion on Hess, and I accordingly forwarded my observations with such a request on May 23rd and again on May 24th.

"The patient during the next few days became at times very depressed, and thought that he must have been misinformed regarding the urgent desire of Britain for an understanding with his Government. At other times there were flashes of a domineering mood, and at exercises he would hold himself erect and strut for the benefit of the guard on duty. At such times his reactions to remarks were characteristic. Thus, if it were suggested that Germany in her calculations failed to take

B

into account the value of help from U.S.A., he would impatiently say: 'All discounted,' and then proceed to dilate on the wealth of material captured in the fall of France. During such moods he was quick to use the propaganda which his colleague, Dr. Joseph Goebbels, spread so industriously. Two examples of many will suffice. If asked about concentration camps he would laugh sarcastically and refer us to the South African War and say: 'You should know, you invented them.' To a question about the total occupation by Germany of Czechoslovakia in defiance of the Munich agreement, he remarked that Germany could not allow the menace of strategic aerodromes which were convenient for attack on great German towns. But the general impression one got was of a man under strain and intensely worried.

"On May 28th, on learning of the sinking of the battleship *Bismarck* he became very anxious and looked ill. He asked for a glass of water, complained of a pain in his back, and went to bed. A physical ill was introduced to cover his mental state. He arose two hours later, saying he was better. On hearing that I proposed to let him dine by himself he became greatly agitated, and requested to dine with us as usual and from the same food. The idea of poison had again entered his mind.

"At dinner his appetite was excellent, and while he had to be restrained from over-eating, he selected his food carefully, suspecting that it had been tampered with. He did not enter into conversation, was morose, and retired to bed early, saying he felt confused and worried. He asked for a sedative.

"During the night he became nervous and distressed, and visited the inside duty officer, requesting whisky (he is a tee-totaller normally). Within half an hour he was back, recounting his reasons for coming to England and wishing to see the Duke of Hamilton. He then went on to say that he believed that the Secret Service at the behest of a 'clique of war-mongers' had hidden him in his present surroundings and were trying to drive him to insanity or suicide.

"Hess then said that during the past few days a devilish scheme had been started to prevent him sleeping at night and resting during the day. Noises were made continuously and deliberately to prevent him sleeping—doors were opened and shut loudly, and people ran up and down uncarpeted stairs, the guard kept clicking his heels; motor-cycles were kept running up and down in front of the house to prey on his nerves, and aeroplanes were flown over the house to disturb him. It was all a plot.

"When I visited him on the morning of May 29th, he was still agitated, and repeated his suspicions and anxieties above about a devilish plot to make his life unendurable by means of motor-bicycles and aeroplanes, etc.

"In view of the rapid deterioration in the patient's mental condition, I added a further report (May 29th), and recommended investigation by a psychiatrist.

"In response to this request he was visited by the consulting psychiatrist, Brigadier J. R. Rees, who agreed that the case required such supervision. Accordingly I handed over the case to Major Dicks, R.A.M.C., on June 1st, 1941."

OPINION AND SUMMARY

1. Although no evidence of mental instability was noted at the beginning of my care of Rudolf Hess, as time went on his behaviour and reactions led me to form the opinion that one dealt with a psychopathic personality.
2. He showed marked hypochondriacal, paranoid tendencies, apprehension and delusions of persecution. Simple incidents were misinterpreted and given a sinister meaning.
3. From such knowledge as I possessed of his flight to this country, his mission was the outcome of his mentally disordered state. The short account of his life he gave me suggested, even as a young man, an abnormal mentality. He showed a lack of sane grasp of affairs, and his motives were vague and incoherent.

This ends Lt.-Col. Graham's professional responsibility for the patient.

Since first impressions are useful in getting hold of a picture such as Hess presented at this time, part of the first report by the consulting psychiatrist is quoted verbatim. This report to the authorities was made after a visit on May 30th, 1941.

"I explained my visit on the grounds that he had been sleeping badly and showing signs of worry and he accepted this very naturally. Our interview was at a quite friendly level and he was calm throughout. At times he was a good deal hampered in explaining his feelings by the language difficulty, for I have no German. (I hope that this difficulty will be entirely overcome by the arrangement which has now been made.)

"As regards his health, the outstanding symptoms at the present time are his insomnia and his depression. He has, he told me, had bouts of insomnia associated with worry over pressure of work ever since the beginning of the war, but he says he was a good sleeper before that. He would normally take his homeopathic drugs for this condition, and when it was worse he would take Phanodorm (a perfectly ordinary preparation used also in this country, of which I am trying to obtain a small supply). At the present time, he says, he is sleeping only about three or four hours, though the night reports say that with the sedative draught he is getting rather more sleep than this. He is not getting any disturbing dreams. He is depressed at the present time, though I was told, and his own story confirms it, that he was less depressed yesterday than he has been recently. My impression is that the depression can be adequately accounted for as the result of his sense of failure of his plans and that it does not give any indication of a seriously diseased state of mind, but that at the same time it might easily get worse and give rise to an attempt at suicide. He has the facies and the slow manner of speaking of a man suffering from a depression.

"His ankle is now giving him no trouble, and his back, he says, is very much better though it had given him some pain a couple of days before, due, I gather, more to his emotional upset when he heard about the *Bismarck* than to any increased physical strain. He told me about his chest wound in the last war, and his abdominal and gall bladder trouble, matters which have been adequately dealt with by Colonel Graham in his reports.

"Our conversation inevitably led to his talking about his plans and their frustration. He said several times that he was, like everyone in Germany, completely convinced about the result of the war, and that Germany must win by the use of her submarines and aircraft. He said that he, and the Fuehrer also, had always disliked the idea of war with England, and had thought it unnecessary. (I was not, of course, pressing him to talk on these matters at all, nor did I comment on them.) He told me how, since the beginning of the bombing of England, the idea of the needless slaughter had weighed on his mind, and also the destruction of the ports and factories. He said that for six months this plan had been in his mind to come to England and make contact with what he had believed was a very large group of people wanting peace. The Fuehrer would not consider anything of the sort and would never have allowed it. He had made his plans and borrowed Willi Messerschmidt's plane on the plea that he wanted it 'for the sport' to make long flights over Germany. He had made several. Only his adjutant knew of this plan of coming to England. He told me that he had left a letter for Hitler.

"I was not, of course, cross-questioning him in any way about this material, which did not seem new, and which was not specifically my concern, but, having a good deal of experience in dealing not merely with neurotics but with delinquents and criminals from the courts in peace-time, I got a strong impression that the story was in general true. In so far as I had had any previous theory in my mind it had been definitely different, and yet on such facts as I had before me I got a certain impression of the genuineness of this story. Hess's lack of fluency in English makes it difficult, I should judge, for him to tell a convincing story that is completely untrue, and at times when he spoke of the slaughter, etc., there was emphasis and feeling in his voice that I felt sure was not simulated. There probably are many facts which I do not know about the circumstances of this visit, and further evidence may be collected which may point in a different direction. These might quite naturally modify the impression that I formed.

"Hess spoke a good deal about his discontent; the absence of books for which he had asked; the lack of news, which he can't understand; and the presence of bars and locks, which he evidently feels are unseemly for a man who has 'come with a flag of truce' and who is 'of flag rank'. He showed traces of suspicion about the various noises of which he complains—the machine-gun practice in a neighbouring camp; the motor-cycles (the Military Police Training Camp);—and the aeroplanes which fly over. This trace of suspicion has evidently been very much more marked, according to Colonel Graham's story, and I think this suspicious tendency is pathological and not entirely to be explained by his unusual circumstances. He showed what was to me an extraordinary lack of insight and failure to realise his position. He also seemed to have no obvious appreciation of the impossible nature of his self-imposed task. He said twice to me 'the King of Britain would never let these things happen', and he was clearly surprised that the Duke of Hamilton had not forthwith arranged for him to talk to the King and that he could not see the Duke of Hamilton and Mr. Kirkpatrick whenever he wished. Though he did not say so to me, the implication was that he was in the hands of the 'war-mongers'.

Tentative Conclusions from my interview.

"While this man is certainly not to-day insane in the sense that would make one consider certification, he is mentally sick. He is anxious and tense; he is of a somewhat paranoid type, i.e., he has suspicions for which there is no sufficient indication in his situation and which persist despite very full explanation. He has an abnormal lack of insight or self-criticism. He is also of an introspective and somewhat hypochondriacal type. He is obviously an intelligent man, and the consequent impression is of a somewhat confused condition in which there are both hysterical and paranoid tendencies. Whilst his judgment on ordinary matters of fact might be sound, his appreciation of more intangible problems would be unsound because of the intrusion of his own personal emotional difficulties. This man gives me the impression of being lacking in balance, a psychopathic personality, to use a technical word, and also of being someone who, because of the added depression due to his circumstances, might take impulsive action such as an attempt at suicide despite his alleged promise to the Fuehrer not to take his life.

"After seeing Hess I had a further chance to hear and digest some of the facts of observation recorded by Colonel Graham and others. I need not repeat these since they are, of course, set down on paper. There is unmistakable evidence of his neurotic tendencies, and he has developed a mild delusional system though it is not at present sufficiently marked or unshakable to justify certification (had he been an ordinary patient). His moodiness and his tendency to slip easily into hysterical symptoms, as after the *Bismarck* news, and his tendency to posturing, are worthy of note. I was told that while the troops were parading in the garden he was on the terrace and that he gave the most curious display by doing what was practically a goose step down the path in front of them as though to demonstrate his own military status and technique. This seems to be important because it probably epitomises the situation. The man has excellent intelligence, but he is childish in his outlook and consequently unstable and with bad judgment. He has clearly been dominated by many people, quack practitioners of various kinds, and most markedly by Professor Haushofer, whose dreams or visions of his (Hess's) mission have been accepted as prophetic.

Diagnosis.

"In my opinion Hess is a man of unstable mentality and has almost certainly been like that since adolescence. In technical language I should, on my present acquaintanceship, diagnose him as a psychopathic personality of the schizophrenic type, i.e., a tendency to a splitting of his personality. He is, as many of these people are, suggestible and liable to hysterical symptom formation. Because of his constitutional make-up and the kind of life he has led of recent years, he is at present in some danger of a more marked depressive reaction now that he feels frustrated."

The new arrangement referred to in the first quoted paragraph of this report was that Major Dicks should come and live with the patient to be in medical charge. As a psychiatrist, he had the further great advantage of being as fluent in German as in English.

CHAPTER IV

THE FIRST PHASE OF CAPTIVITY

First Impressions.

DICKS took over from Gibson Graham on the last Saturday in May, when the prisoner had just arrived in his new and more permanent home of confinement, a somewhat ramshackle and neglected Victorian country house on the edge of a famous military training area.

Before proceeding to a description of the prisoner as he struck the psychiatric observer, it would be well to give some impression of the atmosphere which this country mansion made on a newcomer. This obviously has a bearing in that the detective novel atmosphere necessarily surrounding this place of mystery cannot be disregarded in a discussion of possible paranoid reactions on Hess's part. Even to the newcomer who was not to be closely confined here, the place bore a forbidding enough aspect. It had an outer perimeter of barbed wire patrolled by military police, all traffic being diverted from neighbouring lanes. The only access was by a drive, the entrance to which was a veritable concealed strongpoint with slit-trenches and earthworks, where one's credentials were closely scrutinised. Inside the grounds was an inner perimeter of barbed wire capable of being flood-lit by powerful electric flares, and with an obvious system of bells running along the circumference. This perimeter was again closely patrolled by army sentries. Weapon pits were concealed at many points in this perimeter. A second scrutiny took place at the sentry-box which barred the entrance to the house. Inside the house more wire cages separated that part of the building to which the prisoner was permitted access from the rest of the house, containing the kitchens and serveries in addition to the lounges and dining-room constituting the officers' mess. Inside the house it was strangely quiet on this rainy Saturday afternoon.

One's foot would strike a Tommy-gun concealed under the sofa of the officers' lounge, ready for instant use.

The house had been refurnished in haste and furnished with heavy antique pieces from the Ministry of Works' store in an endeavour to produce an atmosphere of dignified comfort, not so much for the sake of the prisoner as for those officers who were to spend an existence almost as closely confined and secret in this somewhat dingy mansion. People on the whole spoke in low tones and referred to the prisoner as "he" or "that man". His official "top secret" name in documents was "Jonathan", or "J". One learned that the prisoner was never left unattended, especially on his passage from his own rooms upstairs to the mess downstairs. At this stage an attempt at escape or rescue by paratroops or a flying squad of fifth columnists were chiefly feared.

The political officers attached to the prisoner personally, of whom there were three, managed to enhance the sense of mystery and "hush-hush" by impressing on all comers the necessity for the utmost secrecy and discretion in accordance with their instructions. The psychiatrist suddenly found himself a participant in the inner history of world events.

From Col. Graham's account, it became fairly clear that, whilst the patient had made light of his physical injuries to the ankle and spine, he was showing a number of clearly persecutory symptoms which have already been detailed above. In essence, these symptoms fell into two sorts: one which was concerned with the secret plot to poison him, or alternatively to destroy his peace of mind by calculated disturbances of his rest by the use of sounds of aeroplanes, motor-cycles and machine-guns for this purpose. On the other hand, he was also dogged by internal complaints not wholly attributed to the poison which he felt was being administered to him and apparently consisting of abdominal "cramps", fatigue and the subjective sense of "damage to his liver". It was apparently for these internal symptoms that he had brought with him a fantastic array of little pills and nostrums and nature-cure remedies. This led one to the supposition that at least part of the hypochondriacal system had antedated his journey to Britain.

Introduction of Hess.

The political officers and the commandant of the "camp" met in conference with the psychiatrist to draw up a plan of campaign. It was important at this stage that the prisoner should not be aware that he was being watched by a mental specialist. The task of the psychiatrist was complicated by the political aspects of the case. Hess's legal status had not yet been defined; we were uncertain whether the Government would treat him as a prisoner of war or as a prisoner of State. It was hoped that he might make important revelations of German plans and intentions and so we might obtain many vital intelligence data from him. His insightless condition demanded that for these important reasons his pride should not be insulted by our considering him a mental patient. The task of the psychiatrist was therefore defined as discreet supervision and, as far as possible, diagnosis and help to the camp officials in managing him and to the political officers in collecting what useful information they could from him. The psychiatrist therefore was to be simply the camp doctor sent to replace the present medical attendant, who had to return to his military hospital in Scotland.

With these considerations in mind, the psychiatrist was ushered into the presence of the Deputy Fuehrer in his lounge on the first floor. It is fair to say that the first glimpse of Hess produced an immediate reaction—"typical schizophrenic". He was found sitting behind a table littered with papers, his skull-like face wearing a profoundly unhappy, grim expression, with his eyes staring into infinity. The contrast between photographs previously seen in the illustrated papers and the man as he now appeared was prodigious. He was gaunt, hollow-cheeked, pale and lined; whereas the full face produced an impression of baleful strength, the profile disclosed a receding forehead, exaggerated supra-orbital ridges covered with thick bushy eyebrows, deeply sunken eyes, irregular teeth which tended to be permanently bared over the lower lip in the manner of "buck" teeth, a very weak chin and receding lower jaw. The ears were misshapen and placed too low in relation to the height of the eyes. In parenthesis it should be added that a subsequent examination showed the palate to be narrow and arched. The whole man produced the impression of a caged great ape, and "oozed" hostility and suspicion. He was barely civil and, when the officer effecting the introduction withdrew, there was an awkward tense feeling.

However, interest and participation could be induced by the offer of medical help, which produced a momentary reaction of grudging gratitude. With the establishment of rapport, even during this first interview, the private personality of Hess left one with the impression of pathos rather than hostility. He began complaining that he had come here with the best of intentions and had received scurvy and unchivalrous treatment by the nation it was his intention to save from certain destruction. He revealed a split between his "official" attitude as an important representative of the strongest power of Europe and his private simplicity. His personal equipment was of the simplest; his watch was of steel, his linen and other personal accoutrements simple and modest. He produced pictures of his wife and little son and described his interests as those of a mountaineer who had no greater wish than to return to a little chalet where he could devote himself to the education of his child and to countrified pursuits. His interests had been in philosophy and matters of health and welfare. He took a special interest in a rehabilitation centre for disabled industrial workers which he said was his own creation. There was a schoolboy-like pride in his attitude when he related details of his flight, which he said was made secretly without the Fuehrer's knowledge. A mischievous smile came upon his face when he said that in fact the Fuehrer had extracted from all his immediate entourage a promise not to fly, because of the risk of losing his best men through accident. This promise had been given in the first instance for a year, and Hess said that the year had just ended and, as the Fuehrer had forgotten to renew the promise, he had felt absolved from this obligation. In addition to this childishly jesuitical reasoning, he displayed a simple vanity in asking whether the B.B.C. had broadcast his arrival in all detail, and whether, in particular, they had brought the crofter who found him to the microphone.

Outside his spheres of interest he showed a curious lack of contact with ordinary things. He had never played tennis and did not even know how to score in the game, and it transpired during a brief walk we took in the grounds that he did not know the names of extremely common garden flowers. His mind returned again and again to the insult to his dignity and to the fixed idea that his confinement as a prisoner was due to a narrow clique of war-mongers centred on Winston Churchill which had kept him from establishing contact with a large movement for peace and friendship with Germany. This large movement, he thought, permeated the chivalrous Court circles around the throne, of which he had made the Duke of Hamilton the symbol. Even at this early stage it became clear that to him the British world was divided into a wicked circle who were out to foil him and a good, chivalrous circle who would be amenable to his purposes. His knowledge of British life proved to be very limited and inaccurate and based on propaganda clichés.

Here it should be interposed that the arrangements inside the mansion might have contributed to the encouragement of this duality. Hess's own mess consisted, in addition to himself, of the three officers of the Political Intelligence Service and his doctor. The second mess consisted of the commandant and regimental officers of the detachment of the Brigade of Guards responsible for the security of his person and of the camp. Hess was flattered by the fact that he was guarded by "His Majesty's own Bodyguard", among whom he saw a number of typical handsome young officers of aristocratic appearance, who did such duties as escorting him, inspecting the guard, etc. He was suspicious on the other hand of his own immediate attendants, senior men in uniform sufficiently different from those of the guards and speaking German far too well for his peace of mind. It will be seen later on that this duality assumed great importance in the development of his paranoid reaction.

The doctor was clearly no person to whom he was going to confide any political information. All attempts to draw him on this point drew a blank. The only exception to this was an occasion on the first day of our meeting, when the sound of a distant bugle provided an opportunity to point out the childishness of some military practices, and for the observation to be made to him that the British on the whole had very little use for military life, ending with the comment: "Somebody or other has said that you can do everything with bayonets except sit on them." To this Hess retorted immediately and eagerly: "Yes,

yes, that was Napoleon, but he did try it just the same; of course, in the end he came a cropper."*

The first meal in the mess provided evidence, which was to be repeated on many subsequent occasions, of the strength of Hess's poisoning fears, which were sufficiently great to obtrude themselves into his behaviour. An orderly served soup in plates. It was the practice to serve first the senior officer acting as president of the mess, then the prisoner and then the rest of us. When all had been so served, Hess quickly interchanged his own plate with that of the president. During the meat course (on this occasion slices of beef on a dish) he took some bits as far removed as possible from the top piece, to which in the normal course of events he should have helped himself. On subsequent occasions he was liable to change his plate with someone else for this type of course also. Another notable feature was his capriciousness in the matter of food. He would refuse a course or take only a little potato and greens. When sufficiently urged by other people in the manner in which a child might be cajoled, he would then heap an enormous portion on his plate and eat ravenously. He would also sometimes save, for example, pieces of bread and cheese which would have to be taken up to his room. This capriciousness was accounted for on his own evidence by constant conflict between greed and the fear that his inside would retaliate by giving him cramps or other forms of indigestion. He was particularly careful about drinks. In 1941 the officers' mess administered by the Brigade of Guards were still in the fortunate position of being able to supply quite decent table wines—an opportunity of which we were all quick to take advantage! Hess out of natural courtesy was, of course, also offered his glass of wine, but stubbornly refused, as he did coffee and tea, nearly always with the ironical comment that he had to be careful when and what he drank.

In the evening of the first day, when he was in bed, the opportunity was taken to make a physical examination. In addition to the stigmata of degeneration already described, his round-shouldered, narrow-chested physique was noted. By this time his ankle was giving practically no trouble, but he was

---

* Verbatim German: "Ja, ja, das war Napoleon, aber er hat es doch versucht. Ist·ihm ja aber zuletzt auch schiefgegangen."

very gratified at the close attention being given to his physical well-being. He now disclosed that he had difficulty in sleeping and asked for alleviation. He produced requests for a number of herbal and nature-cure remedies with which orthodox medical practice in this country was not acquainted. Without power to insist on his taking them, he was supplied with tablets of medinal, which he promised to take, pending the arrival of Phanodorm, a preparation in which he had confidence

In summing up the confused impressions of the first contact with Hess, certain points clearly emerged.

1. The existence of a paranoid attitude towards his present surroundings only partly accounted for by reality, and of a long-standing hypochondriacal preoccupation with his own health and internal bodily processes for which he sought cranky rather than ordinary treatment.

2. The existence of a fixed division of his environment into evil persecuting forces and good and helpful forces, notable for the *a priori* nature of such beliefs.

3. The generally fantastic background to his thinking.

4. The curious mixture of official haughtiness and anxiety to maintain status on the one hand with personal modesty and simplicity on the other hand.

5. The general impression of having his mind fixed on some far-away inner topics which was apt to produce a sense of withdrawnness and lack of contact with reality, except in certain narrow segments of experience in which his inner world and his outer interests fused.

At this stage it might be useful also to add some non-medical comments by the highly intelligent and cultured group of guards officers who had seen a good deal of him. Among them may be quoted: "I think this man is worth about £2/10/0 in the open labour market!" "What a dull dog!" Other comments in somewhat un-parliamentary language referred to his lack of manners, his surliness and his hysterical childish attitude towards food.

In view of the sinister psychiatric possibilities, safety measures were at once overhauled and, whilst it was at this stage obviously impossible to introduce mental nurses, it was decided that an

officer of the guard should spend the night in the room
adjoining Hess's bedroom and inspect him at frequent intervals
on the plea of protecting him. A supply of drugs, such as a
choice of barbiturates, morphia and chloralamide and pot.
brom., was ordered, as well as a number of other medicines with
a possibly rational therapeutic action, such as tincture of
belladonna, gentian and rhubarb and those few of his herbal
remedies which could be obtained in war-time London, e.g.,
camomile tea. All possible steps were taken to ensure that the
reality basis for his paranoid suspicions should be reduced to a
minimum. In the manner of serving food he should always be
given a free choice, in the assurance given by officers guarding
him and in the attitude to be taken by the officers attached to
him his fears could at least be rationally reduced. The commandant issued orders for the elimination of unnecessary
noises which the patient might interpret as deliberately aimed
at him. We were aware, however, that nothing we could do was
likely to diminish to any great extent what was obviously a well-
established persecutory system in Hess's mind.

The Collection of Evidence for Diagnosis.

During the next fortnight there was ample opportunity for
observing the prisoner, although very little opportunity for
systematic examination because he was preoccupied with
preparing his paper for the British Cabinet. His behaviour
served to pile up the evidence showing that we were dealing
with an abnormal personality in whom suspicion was exaggerated beyond anything to be expected in a prisoner,
ambivalence very marked, and reality thinking disturbed by
the incursion of paranoid fantasies.

It was difficult to say whether the paranoid projection
mechanisms or the hypochondriacal introjection mechanisms
played a greater part in his make-up—they were so evenly
balanced. He repeated many of the suspicions and fantasies
which he had already mentioned to Gibson Graham and, as he
gained confidence in his new doctor, the details of his persecutory fantasies became clear. The secret enemy who was
attempting to poison him might, he said, be for example some

German-Jewish immigrant acting for international Jewry.
This man might easily have obtained access to one of the
kitchen staff, who would then introduce poison into his food.
He could therefore not risk failure of his peace mission by
exposing himself to the machinations of such evil people. He
felt sure that all the officers surrounding him were perfect
gentlemen in His Britannic Majesty's service, who would of
course not know anything about this plot. He gradually
shifted his ground, under constant persuasion from his officers
in attendance, in acknowledging that the noises of motor-
cycles, aircraft, etc., might be accidental, to a new complaint
that members of the household were purposely keeping him
awake by slamming doors, sudden shouts, etc., which he was
convinced were engineered in order to disturb his rest and so
exhaust his mind. These ideas were found to be proof against
logical argument. In fact, the more strictly quiet was observed,
the more would any accidental noise impinge on his consciousness and be further proof of the correctness of his sur-
mises. From time to time, however, he would apologise for
making so much fuss about the question of noise and thank us
for stopping some particular one. He would then add that he
realised these noises had not been engineered maliciously.
Despite the giving of standard sedatives and sleeping tablets,
the provision of ear plugs and other measures, the prisoner
suffered continually from wakefulness. He did not apparently
resent the frequent inspection visits of the night duty officer,
however.

During the first days no one in particular among his entourage was definitely associated with the hidden conspiracy.
The symptoms of changing plates at meal-times and of complaining about noises occurred intermittently. At this stage
indeed other symptoms of the introspective and anxiety type
were perhaps more prominent. Thus it emerged that for years
he had been afraid of being passively conveyed in a motor-car
or train and that he only liked travel if he himself was the driver.
This symptom is frequently observed among claustrophobics.
It also became clear that he was an extremely punctilious man
of precise habits, who lived by the clock. He would always rise
at the same time and resent intrusion into his bedroom a
moment earlier than the hour he had anticipated. He would

go for a stroll in the somewhat confined grounds at a set time and carry it out in the same routine fashion, almost visibly counting his steps in one direction, then, turning in military fashion, he would march down to the other end; his little rituals and fads at meal-times were soon to assume a stereo-typed pattern; his fear of indulgence has already been remarked upon and, quite apart from his fear of being poisoned, there was always the ritual of protestation against indulgence, over which he had to be coaxed. He wished it to be known that he was a man of plain and (abstemious) habits, thinking of his digestion and the avoidance of unpleasant internal sensations. This hypochondriacal preoccupation with his physiological pro-cesses was, on his own evidence, one of long standing. He confided to us that for years he had carefully followed out Rudolf Steiner's injunctions about not eating vegetables grown under artificial conditions, and that he had had a special greengrocer who delivered farm produce reared on natural manure. This opening into the world of the occult provided an opportunity for observing that he had for years been interested in Steiner's anthroposophy and related magical topics, notably astrology and the prophecies based upon it, as well as in her-balist lore, which to some extent is founded upon the mystical doctrine of "correspondences".

A strange rationalisation was frequently observed. Whereas he was aware that he had had his symptoms of abdominal discomfort and fatigue for some time, he would tell us that he saw proof of the working of the secret poison conveyed to him by the unknown Jewish conspiracy in the sense of increased well-being after meals which was followed by sudden subjective exhaustion. In fact, so subtle was this poison given to him that it actually at times made him feel better, and this he thought was part of the devilry of his enemies.

As to the background and motives for his flight he maintained considerable reserve and replied to enquiries by saying that he would only disclose his intentions to properly authorised representatives of the British Government. He spent a great part of his days in preparing an elaborate written statement of his arguments to be used when and if the negotiators appeared. These he always wrote in indelible pencil, with a carbon copy, and they were models of clarity, of exposition and logical argument. From time to time he would also lodge a written complaint to the protecting power, i.e., the Swiss minister, which would be a statement of the evidence on which he based his conviction that he was being purposely tormented, poisoned or prevented from sleeping.

His rapport with, and confidence in, any given person of his entourage always remained woefully small. After short intervals of conversation with him one received the strong impression that "His Excellency" was no longer amused and would be glad to dismiss his companion. Sometimes this would be done by a groan, followed by shutting his eyes and stroking his forehead to indicate that he was exhausted. From time to time his complaint of exhaustion would be made explicitly with a surprised shrugging of the shoulders and a query: "I cannot understand why I should be so tired—what is it? I am very worried."

Much of the spare time not taken up by preparing his case for the British negotiators he would occupy by making neat and detailed plans for his future ideal mountain residence—an activity we have since found to be favoured by many German prisoners of war. It appears that he was something of a gadgeteer, who would delight in fantasies of hidden knobs working concealed wirelesses, sliding doors and tricks of illumination, the meaning of which will not elude the psycho-pathologist. This fantasy of his own inviolable home in which he could entertain and shape life exactly as he wanted it was perhaps his best moral support during this phase of his captivity. The dream house was, however, a very egocentric project in which his study and the public reception rooms played a much greater part than his wife's bedroom or his son's nursery. He gave the impression constantly that, though a model family man, he was not in fact greatly interested in his wife as a sexual partner or a love object. His letters to his little son, on the other hand, were quite charming, although somewhat pompous considering that this child was only three years old. One had the impression that he was writing these letters of guidance under patriotic inspiration, with an eye to his biography and publication.

The political officers attached to him used to suffer a good deal from his impatience to be brought face to face with a

representative of the Government of a status which he as
Deputy Fuehrer would acknowledge as his equal, and also from
his many complaints about the indignities to which he was
subjected. In point of fact, little time was lost, and within a few
days it was announced that a negotiator of high rank would
arrive in order to hear his proposals on the 10th of June. This
announcement coincided with a remarkable increase in the
prisoner's restlessness and anxiety. So long as that date was
shadowy he could blame us for keeping his message from
reaching the competent British authorities, just as earlier he
had been furious because the Duke of Hamilton had not
arrived or remained with him long enough. Now, by our
demonstration of good faith, it almost looked as if he was faced
with feelings of inadequacy. He complained more frequently of
feeling ill and unable to go through with his task. From time to
time he would say that his head was so bad that he could not
concentrate; that his mind went blank, and so forth. The
psychiatric observer could not help recognising the "neurotic
alibi", as described by Adler. This anxiety and restlessness was
accompanied by obstinate resistance to any form of suggested
remedy, such as more rest, tonics, light treatment, massage,
relaxation and the like, all of which were offered to him in
order to give him the feeling that nothing would be left undone
to give him a fair chance of meeting a spokesman of the British
Government on the best possible terms. It was the impression
of the many cultured and highly intelligent officers surrounding
Hess that he had what is commonly called an "inferiority
complex" and that he cut a very poor figure by comparison
with the average member of the intellectual classes. He
himself made quite pathetic pleas from time to time that he felt
at a disadvantage and that he was no negotiator. It was felt
that he was engineering a complete hysterical breakdown
before the forthcoming negotiations, when his capacity *vis-à-vis*
a first-rate intellect would be put to a severe strain.

It was partly with these considerations in mind that an
attempt was made to administer an intelligence test to him.
The psychiatrist had always differed from the other observers
on the question of the actual level of Hess's intelligence and
taken the view that this was of a fairly high order, but that his
emotional difficulties prevented him from applying it, at least

in the present circumstances. Partly under the guise of a new diversionary game and partly with the avowed aim of reassuring him of his capacity, the Raven's Progressive Matrices Test, then recently put into service in the British Army, was administered to him. He was glad to co-operate, and worked at the test for some twenty-five minutes with intense eagerness and concentration. He filled up the answers to columns A to D in that time without a single mistake, then put down his pencil and, rubbing his forehead in characteristic fashion, announced: "I am sorry, I am so exhausted I can do no more." On this showing, however, it was possible to infer that at least on this test his intelligence was likely to be of the order of Selection Group I, placing him in the upper ten per cent of distribution of intelligence.

As the 10th June approached, the prisoner's condition became more and more alarming, especially as he refused food, and it was necessary to resort to special methods of maintaining his food intake. He rarely came down to meals; these had to be served in his room and we resorted to the expedient of detailing officers of the guard in turn to eat food with him, i.e., we provided him with a poison taster who would leave Hess to pick his food first, but invariably began eating before the prisoner. At this stage Hess also wrote a memorandum for transmission to the Protecting Power, in which he drew up a list of persons involved in a secret conspiracy to poison him. At the top of the list figured Brigadier Rees; next, one of the political officers; and next, the commandant of the camp whose visits to him had always been of the most formal kind, and with whom he had very little contact; and lastly, H. V. Dicks, his present medical attendant. It was interesting to see how one person after another began by drawing his confidence to a considerable degree within the limits possible to his suspicious personality and how each in turn became gradually involved in the conspiracy. As he lost one "friend" so he had to get new ones, and he typically concentrated his feelings of confidence on the young officers of the guard as the King's representatives. To these officers he would contrive to entrust secret missions—documents to be smuggled out of the camp—and, on one occasion, a package of sedatives and sleeping tablets administered by the psychiatrist. These he wished to be taken for secret chemical analysis of the nature of the poison therein contained.

On the morning of June 10th our fears that Hess would stage a breakdown were found to be unjustified. He consented to drink a good deal of milk, dressed with great care in his Air Force uniform, and was in a very confident and almost arrogant mood. There was no medical witness present at the negotiations which, as the world now knows, were carried out on the British side by the then Lord Chancellor, Viscount Simon, assisted by Mr. Ivone Kirkpatrick of the Foreign Office. These negotiations continued for a long period of time, with an interruption for luncheon, at which Hess did not appear. He had asked for a German witness, and this had been granted to him in the shape of some interned minor German Consular official, who must have felt very strange at being suddenly precipitated into this dramatic episode. The details of the negotiations which took place were published in the Press around March 25th, 1946. It is hardly necessary to add that, as we happened to know, there was never any intention of accepting his proposals for a peace, but that the main purpose of this interview was to try and induce him to give away the German position and plans.

Reuter's message from Nuremberg as published in the *Evening Standard* of London on March 25th, 1946, is as follows:

"The 'secret record' submitted by the defence to-day of a three-hour talk between Rudolf Hess and Lord Simon, then Lord Chancellor, shows that it took place on June 10th, 1941— a month after Hess's flight to Scotland.

"In this document Hess is referred to as 'Jay', Lord Simon as 'Dr. Guthrie', and Mr. I. A. Kirkpatrick of the Foreign Office as 'Dr. Mackenzie'.

"Dr. Seidl, Hess's counsel, explained that the cover names were used so that stenographers and translators should not know at the outset what it was all about.

"The defence document does not explain why Lord Simon, who told Hess that he was able to 'receive his mission with Government authority', appeared in this way.

"Cajolery and Threats".

"The record pictures the mixture of persuasiveness, cajolery and threats with which Hess—on his own initiative, if he is to be believed—sought to convince Britain of the necessity for accepting the 'basis of understanding' with Germany which he handed to Lord Simon in writing.

"Hess began by saying that the idea of the flight to Britain occurred to him when he was with Hitler during the French campaign in 1940. He went on:

" 'Convinced as we all were that we would conquer England sooner or later—but in the end certainly—I expressed the opinion to the Fuehrer that we must naturally demand from England the restitution of goods such as the value of the merchant fleet, and so on, which were taken from us by the Versailles Treaty.

"Faced Critical Decision."

" 'The Fuehrer contradicted me immediately. He is of the opinion that the war could possibly lead finally to agreement with England, and he said that even if victorious one should not impose any severe conditions on a country with which it is desired to come to an agreement.

'I thought that if England once knew of this fact it might be possible that England on its part was ready for agreement.'

"Hess, talking almost continuously, with few interjections from the listeners, went on to speak of Hitler's 'offer' to England after the collapse of France and the subsequent development of the air war.

" 'I must confess,' he said, 'that I faced a very critical decision —the most critical decision of my life. I believe it became possible for me through a thought. Not only on the German side, but also on the English side, I continually pictured an endless row of children's coffins with mothers crying behind them, and vice versa, coffins of mothers with children behind them.'

"Hess then warmed up to the familiar Nazi argument, presenting the Versailles Treaty as an unjust 'diktat' shackled on Germany so tightly that even when the Reich was 'a democracy of the purest water' efforts to obtain relief were unavailing.

"Women Reproached Hitler."

"At great length he went over all the German arguments which have been frequently heard from the defence during the trial on Czecho-Slovakia, Poland, Norway and the Low

Countries, with England always as a scapegoat.

"It appears from the record that British air attacks were already having some effect, because Hess said the Fuehrer 'hesitated again and again to order counter-attacks'. He continued:

"'But gradually mothers who had lost their children, families who had lost their relatives reproached the Fuehrer: Why did he not finally retaliate?

"'When the Fuehrer had come to the conclusion that common sense could not prevail in England, he acted just according to the rule of conduct of Admiral Lord Fisher: Moderation in war is folly. If you strike, strike hard and wherever you can.

"'But I can confirm that it was indeed always difficult for the Fuehrer to give orders for these attacks. It pained him deeply. He was constantly in full sympathy with the English people who were victims of this method of waging war.'

"*British, too, are proud.*"

"Here Lord Simon interrupted Hess, saying:

"'Herr Hess will, of course, understand that if I do not contradict or challenge what he says about the war it is not because I agree, but because the real purpose why I have come is to hear from him about his mission.

"'Herr Hess must understand that the British people too are a proud people—"Herrenvolk"—and will not easily accept such reproaches.'

"To this Hess replied: 'My flight was strongly influenced by the fact that the leaders of Germany are absolutely convinced that England's position is helpless.'

"He then launched into an account of the Luftwaffe's expansion, which he had made in his earlier statements to the Duke of Hamilton and Mr. Kirkpatrick.

"'Air personnel which is now coming along is moving about on approximately as large a scale as the entire English expeditionary force in France,' he said.

"When Lord Simon pressed him to put this in figures Hess avoided the question, saying: 'In view of my personal relations with the flying world—Messerschmidt is a friend of mine, and I know all factories and all air chiefs—I have some idea of what will happen to England sooner or later. And that is one of the reasons why I have come here.'

"Lord Simon asked Hess how he reconciled his statement that British bombing was negligible in its effect with his story of the 'bitterness' of raid victims who pressed Hitler for retaliation.

"Hess wriggled at first and then explained he meant 'losses were small in comparison with those suffered in England'.

"Lord Simon: 'Then your message is that you believe there will be in future a far more violent and terrific overwhelming attack on this country?' Hess: 'Yes.'

"Then Hess went on to paint an alarming picture of the development of the German U-boat arm.

"Lord Simon: 'Nothing amuses the British people as much as German figures about sinking British tonnage. It makes them laugh.'

"Hess: 'May be, but I am convinced the day will come when the English people will no longer laugh about it.'

"Lord Simon: 'The day may come, the day may come. But if German official figures are correct, you know it is a pity we are not all dead.'

"Hess went on to talk of the possibility of a British capitulation through lack of tonnage. 'We would not consider occupying the Mother Country because we would have to feed the people there,' he said.

"*Hitler did not know.*"

" 'In the event of a capitulation without occupation, we should only occupy a number of important air bases in the most extreme case, and we would shut them off from the population —the starving population—so that our own soldiers would never see anything of it.'

"Hess continued that whenever he contemplated his flight he always sounded the Fuehrer regarding conditions for peace.

"Lord Simon: 'Do you come here with the Fuehrer's knowledge or without his knowledge?'

"Hess: 'Without his knowledge. Absolutely.'

"After making this reply, Hess laughed and then went on: 'This which I have written down here is what the Fuehrer told me in several conversations.'

"Hess then handed over the 'basis for understanding'—a free hand for Germany in Europe and for Britain in the Empire, return of the German colonies, evacuation of Irak and armistice and peace with Italy.

"At the end of the interview Hess told Lord Simon that if England were not to agree to these conditions 'sooner or later the day will come when we will be forced to accede them.'

"'Lord Simon replied: 'I do not think that that particular argument will be very good for the British Cabinet, because, you know, there is a good deal of courage in this country, and we are not very fond of threats!' "

Reuter.

Medical interest centres on the immediate aftermath of the conference, when Hess was found in a state of virtual collapse in his sitting-room. The reasons for his extreme feelings of exhaustion may only be surmised. The trend of the negotiations had not only proved the overwhelming mental superiority of his British antagonist, but had also convinced him that his plan to split British leading circles and make peace on Germany's conditions had been based on a fantasy. Tea, milk and cake was ordered for him, but he refused all these. A glucose drink was then prepared and offered by the psychiatrist in person. Hess stood up, gazed for a long time into the psychiatrist's eyes and then said: "I will have it if you have some first." The psychiatrist, who had already had a good tea, was forced to demonstrate the harmlessness of both the glucose drink and the cake, whereupon, as usual, Hess ate ravenously and at great speed.

The days that now followed were chiefly noteworthy for the prominence both of symptoms of persecution and of subjective mental exhaustion. So far as the persecutory symptoms are concerned, the patient was tackled on the morning after the incident with the cake and glucose and told that he had made an unworthy and quite unwarranted accusation against his medical attendant who had been charged by his Government to take every possible care of the prisoner. To this Hess replied with a particularly ingenious piece of paranoid thinking. He stated that he regarded Brigadier Rees, the commandant and other officers, as well as the psychiatrist, as men of the greatest honour and integrity who personally felt "very sympathetic to him". The pity was, however, that all of us had unfortunately ourselves fallen under evil influence. He could not say whether this was hypnotic or chemical, whether we were being drugged or influenced in other ways. He knew, however, that we were all the unconscious tools or agents of the secret conspiracy and could not help ourselves in carrying out its wishes in slowly destroying his mental resistance and his physical health. This statement was perhaps the greatest evidence of systematisation, and the involvement of new personalities and increasing circles in the persecutory system.

The prisoner asked for and borrowed a copy of Goethe's works. Shortly after this interview, which ended on a friendly note so far as the psychiatrist personally was concerned, Hess began writing a number of rather high-flown valedictory letters to his relatives and indeed one to the Fuehrer himself, in which he protested once again his complete loyalty to the cause of National Socialism and his abject, filial devotion to Hitler personally. In several of these letters he quoted a poem of unknown authorship.

> "According to eternal, iron, great
> Laws
> Must we all
> Complete the cycles
> Of our being."*

In the same letter to Hitler he showed that he was preparing for death, when he wrote: "I die in the conviction that my last mission, even if it ends in death, will somehow bear fruit. Perhaps my flight will bring, despite my death or indeed partly because of my death, peace and reconciliation with England."†

From this letter it was not clear whether he expected now to be killed, but this seemed to be the most likely interpretation. He was determined that there was to be a heroic, Messiah-like martyrdom of his person for a great cause at the hands of evil-doers, and the "simple grandeur" note of (masochistic) surrender strikes a familiar note both to the clinician and to the student of melodrama.

* Verbatim German:
    "Nach ewigen, ehrnen, grossen
    Gesetzen
    Müssen wir alle
    Unseres Daseins
    Kreise vollenden."

† "Ich sterbe in der Ueberzeugung, dass mein letzter Einsatz, auchwenn er mit dem Tode endet, irgendwie Früchte tragen wird. Vielleicht bringt mein Flug trotz meines Todes, oder gerade mit durch meinen Tod, Frieden und Verständigung mit England."

A strange feature in view of his suspicious attitude was the acceptance at this time of a hot toddy and luminal at night as a soporific, although all forms of relaxation and suggestion treatment that were offered as a help to greater mental composure and sleep were disdainfully refused with every appearance of intense inner anxiety. Hand in hand with this advance in "alimentary" confidence there went a curious cold-shouldering and morose, stony aloofness towards the psychiatrist—almost a refusal to talk or take any notice of him. The condition was one of very great ambivalent tension and anxiety.

One day rather suddenly the psychiatrist was sent for and received by Hess with a solemn request to do his best for him to protect him against harm. This was followed by a promise of most extravagant rewards in money, position and influence if he should be successful in warding off the poisoners; the reward to be implemented in the great days of German victory that lay ahead. It thus seemed that the prisoner was in a state of acute conflict about needing to trust somebody and in true tyrant fashion thinking it necessary to offer handsome remuneration in return for genuine service, but that on the other hand he felt he could trust no one. He was conscious that he had failed and that it was time to say good-bye to life, as the British no longer needed him. Access to him could only be had on his own terms and, like a sulking, angry child, he made his entourage feel that they had forfeited his goodwill. It thus became necessary to think very seriously about suicidal attempts, but it was difficult to carry out anything further than the all but constant supervision which he already had and to make as sure as possible that he was getting adequate sedation. It was only occasionally that one was able to witness his taking of tablets. At most times he would promise to take them when one left him for the night. The reader has to bear in mind that he was still technically a sane and responsible person, and that under the Geneva Convention and medical ethics it was difficult to force drugs or other treatment on an unwilling prisoner, especially one in his mental condition. He stated at various times that he was only getting three or four hours' sleep at night, and asked to be reassured as to the number of hours necessary to maintain health. As he was in a good mood, the reply given was that a few hours' sleep was all that was necessary for physiological restoration, and the example of Napoleon quoted. Not to be outdone, Hess at once said: "Yes, yes, that is true—the Fuehrer only needs three and a half hours," thus going one better than Napoleon by half an hour!

On June 15th the psychiatrist was invited by Hess to go to his room and was confronted by the Deputy Fuehrer standing at the table, glowering, with fists clenched and obviously in a state of great emotional tension. In reply to the enquiry as to what he could do for him, Hess shouted: "I am being undone, and you know it!" Attempting to appear unconcerned, the psychiatrist said to him: "How do you mean—in what way are you being undone?" Whereupon he shouted again: "You know it; you know it!" It was clear that a crisis had been reached in his mental condition. All soothing talk and appeal to reason, such as a review of the many acts of help and proofs of our interest in his continued well-being and health, were completely lost on him. He was in a state verging upon agitation in the technical sense, trembling, pacing the room and yet not vouchsafing any information beyond the dark hint: "You know it."

It was clear that such precautions as we were able to take had to be put on the alert and the night duty officer was warned to be particularly vigilant.

CHAPTER V

THE FIRST ATTEMPT AT SUICIDE

THE atmosphere on the evening of June 15th was very tense and charged with misgiving, and (writes Dr. Dicks) I made a late visit to the patient after he had retired to bed, talking reassuringly to him and urging him to take his sleeping tablets in order to secure a good night's rest. In the small hours of the morning I was awakened by a knock on my bedroom door with a message that Hess wished to see me as he was unable to sleep. I donned my dressing-gown, armed myself with a further supply of sleeping tablets and advanced across the landing.

At this point it is necessary to describe the lay-out of this landing. A large oaken staircase led up to the first floor around a square well. On the side nearest the stairs a wire grille had been erected turning the landing into a narrow passage along which Hess's sitting-room, bedroom and bathroom was disposed. The grille had a door in it which was kept bolted from the outside whenever he was on this floor, and it was guarded by an armed sergeant of Military Police. The officer on night duty was always inside this cage, sitting in the lounge and inspecting Hess in his bedroom frequently. The opening in the grille was almost exactly opposite Hess's bedroom door. My bedroom door was on the opposite side of the landing with the doors of other officers' bedrooms to the right and left.

The message had been that Hess was unable to sleep. As I was advancing along the thirty feet or so separating my bedroom door from the door of the cage, the sergeant of police unbolted this door and swung it outwards towards him. The officer of the guard stood aside between Hess's bedroom door and this opening preparing to let me pass. Suddenly, out of the shadows of his bedroom there emerged the figure of the Deputy Fuehrer, in his full Air Force uniform and flying boots, and dashed towards me through the momentary free passage so created. The expression on his face was one of extreme despair, his eyes staring, his hair dishevelled. From the previous evening's experience I felt sure that he was going to attack me physically. I was about to tackle him when he did a rapid side-step, and took a flying leap over the banister. A heavy thud occurred, after what seemed minutes later, on the floor of the hall, followed by agonised groans. The whole incident on the landing could not have lasted more than three seconds, but such was one's heightened appreciation of reality that I had noted a second sergeant of the guard coming up the stairs bringing a cup of tea for his colleague on watch. As Hess leapt, the tea-cup clattered to the ground and the sergeant had already drawn his revolver and I had time to shout "don't fire!"

We now rushed downstairs to the recumbent figure of the prisoner, who was groaning and shouting: "Morphia, give me morphia!" He was fully conscious, and offered no kind of resistance. Immediate examination of the pulse and re-spiration showed that he was not very badly shocked. From all doors poured members of the household—officers, orderlies, and members of the inside guard of the building. Hess himself pointed to his thigh as the site of the pain, and was able to tell me that he was a fool because he had failed in his leap to take into account the fact that his fall would be broken by the hand-rail of the lower flight of stairs. He claimed that he had taken a header, but in fact I observed him leaping over the banister in "hurdler" style. His left leg had struck the oaken rail, and he had then fallen relatively softly to the stone floor of the hall.

The domestic staff, with characteristic kindliness, were producing pillows and blankets and the inevitable cups of tea. Within a few minutes of repeated pulse and respiration taking it became clear that the patient had sustained no major internal injuries, but there was clearly a fracture of the femur on the left side. The limb was as far as possible immobilised where he was lying and treatment for shock given, with Hess himself interestedly supervising arrangements in a very businesslike manner. His reactions were a curious mixture of schoolboy interest with annoyance at having failed in his attempt and a certain desire to manage other people.

A call was immediately sent to the surgical specialist of a neighbouring military hospital, to hold himself in readiness to be met by the car and brought to our secret location. Until he had made his diagnosis I was not prepared to administer morphia for fear of masking symptoms and signs of internal injury. The patient thus had to be humoured for about one and a half hours, during which from time to time he would resume groaning and imperiously demanding morphia. His condition steadily improved so far as shock and warmth were concerned, but he was naturally in considerable pain. I therefore administered a suitable amount of distilled water hypodermically. The suggestive effect was entirely negative, and within a few minutes Hess stated that he had been deceived, as this was not morphia. In general, however, this period of waiting for the surgeon revealed the fact that his mental state had become one of a resigned calm and a quiet friendly co-operation with his helpers, who included a sergeant with some previous nursing experience. He was grateful and almost hilarious in manner.

The surgical specialist, Major J. B. Murray, M.S., F.R.C.S., after thorough examination confirmed the absence of thoracic or abdominal injury, and made the diagnosis of an uncomplicated fracture of the upper part of the left femur, which he proceeded there and then to put up in a temporary Thomas's splint, having been warned to bring the necessary apparatus.

At this stage the only noteworthy reactions on Hess's part were his chagrin at having his beautiful breeches cut open with scissors and his docile childlike trust in and co-operation with Major Murray. There was no suspicion on his part of any of the countless hot drinks that had been given as part of his shock treatment, and the atmosphere remained one of calm. Fortunately Major Murray was able to agree to the treatment of the fracture in Hess's own bedroom, where he was now transferred on the sturdy shoulders of a number of guardsmen. Morphia was administered and the patient made comfortable pending the arrival of a mobile X-ray unit and the apparatus for permanent treatment of the fracture.

In the afternoon of that day Major Rigby, R.A.M.C., confirmed by radiography the favourable position of the fragments, which were very little displaced, and the fact that the only other injury had been a crack in one of the thoracic vertebral spinous processes. Under (evipan) anæsthesia, the fragments were placed in alignment and the limb put up in an extension secured by a Steinmann pin introduced into the tibia, with Balkan frame and weights over pulleys. The bed was converted into a proper fracture bed. By the late afternoon two expert nursing orderlies with both general and mental nursing qualifications had already reported for duty. Hess was comfortable and at peace until the late evening, when the common symptoms of retention of urine began to bother him. Ordinary measures having failed, he himself asked for catheterisation. At about midnight I was ready to carry out this measure with a soft, gum-elastic catheter when Hess suddenly demanded that the urethra should first be anæsthetised with cocaine. This was unfortunately not available, as it had not from my experience occurred to me as a necessity. Reassuring him that this would not be required I made to introduce the catheter. The patient hereupon raised a tremendous hue and cry, shouting "help, help!" Once again, scenting further drama, the denizens of our house of mystery poured from all the doors, with myself torn between my duties to the patient and my wish to reassure a group of officers who had been already considerably upset by the day's incidents and their narrowly averted prospects of unpleasant courts of enquiry and displeasure in high places. After calming the officers with a jest, I returned to Hess and, partly from irritation, having by this time been on duty for some twenty hours, and partly deliberately, said to him: "Aren't you ashamed of yourself? You, the second man in the German Reich, causing us all this trouble and then bellowing like a baby; I shall do nothing further to relieve your bladder." The reward was a baleful glance, an immediate cessation of the noise, and in due course a natural evacuation of the bladder.

The surgical progress of the patient henceforth was uninterrupted, with the surgeon visiting him from time to time, and no complications of any kind arose from the fracture. From the angle of the management of the patient, this potentially unfortunate episode had two advantages. Firstly, for various reasons which will be taken up in the section in which the case as a whole is discussed, the suicidal attempt was followed by a phase of calm and disappearance of the symptoms. Moreover, we were now for the moment dealing with an overt case of mental illness recognised as such by the politicians, and were able to enforce a proper psychiatric regime. The political aspect of the case receded. Lastly, from the point of view of security, the commandant and his staff were also relieved by the enforced recumbency of their charge. Supervision became a purely medical responsibility, and we did not need to conceal our efforts in this direction.

With the change in regime, during which we were able to search Hess's belongings in order to take away his razors and other dangerous objects, while turning his bedroom into a combination of surgical home and psychiatric isolation cell, we came across his hoard of sleeping tablets. One had suspected that he had not taken them, but had never found any evidence. It would have been most inexpedient to search his room in the early days whilst he was still a possibly valuable source of political information. Hess's mental state for the next few days was a welcome relief to the tension and excitement of the previous phase. During this time he was able to discuss his suicidal attempt in semi-rational terms. Granted the assumption that he was being persecuted, he said, he would rather be dead than made insane and slowly done to death by his enemies. At the same time, after relatively slight argument, he conceded that all his fears might have been subjective and used himself the word "a psychosis" (a term which in German usage does not necessarily carry the implication of insanity when used by laymen). He was docile and forthcoming in all matters pertaining to the care of his fracture and co-operated well with the team of excellent mental nursing orderlies who joined the establishment. In view of his now relatively normal state and our complete clinical control over him, it was also judged wise to allow him access to world news in the shape of a daily copy of *The Times*, which for a few days he read avidly, but talked about only with officers of the guard (one of whom still continued to act as his food taster) or with his nursing orderlies. One of the political officers spent long daily periods with him in a genuine endeavour to dismiss his suspicions on the excellent ground that if we had wished for his death we would have seized this opportunity to neglect his fracture, whereas in fact everything possible was being done to heal it.

This relatively quiet and insightful phase of relief of tension did not, however, last long. On July 19th it was found that he expressed once again his delusions of persecution and a plot against his life and against his sanity, and moreover stated that

c

he would make further attempts as soon as opportunity came. He also threatened that he would go on hunger strike, but this situation never actually arose at this time owing to the devoted services of the nursing orderlies, with one of whom at least he developed a particularly close rapport.

It was this orderly who reported what constitutes the only slender evidence of Hess's suffering at this time from hallucinations. The orderly, an experienced and sensitive man, sitting with him in the day-time, had observed Hess, apparently in a state of repose, suddenly turn his head and eyes towards some corner of the ceiling and look intently as if straining to identify some sound. The orderly recognised this behaviour as similar to that he had seen in other patients known to be hallucinated. The point is here noted for what it is worth.

The nursing arrangements were now from the psychiatrist's point of view ideal; six excellent men were at his disposal who worked in eight-hour shifts in pairs, one of them permanently within a few feet of the patient. Every possible precaution was taken to keep possible objects of danger out of Hess's reach. Only unbreakable materials and blunt eating utensils were permitted. From this point of view it was felt that the patient, however excited he might become, could be easily controlled. Arrangements were put in hand for guarding against all future contingencies when he should be up and about again.

It might be interesting to record Hess's reaction on the 22nd June, when the psychiatrist on his morning visit told him of the invasion of the Soviet Union. His sole response was a very wan, wry smile and the words: "So they have started after all." When further pressed for his opinions, he took the expected attitude, that we would no doubt see rapid developments and hinted that it would not be long before Germany would be completely victorious in that theatre and would then be able to turn her full attention to the defeat of Great Britain. In the main, he was very uncommunicative on these matters, although he followed proceedings in *The Times* with more interest than he was willing to admit. Not infrequently, however, he was so much preoccupied with his own internal tensions that he hardly opened the paper.

A few days later, the patient, despite the superficial façade of outward co-operativeness and docility, wrote a lengthy deposition which he tried to smuggle past the commandant by naïvely making a confidant of one of the Guards' officers, who was to deliver copies to the King and to Parliament. The prisoner confirmed in writing his suspicions that a number of the officers surrounding him were being hypnotised and used by an evil power to encompass his destruction. His insight had thus completely vanished again, and he went so far in that document as to accuse these officers of being themselves insane.

A notable feature of this lying in bed phase was the way in which he would single out one of the number of Guards' officers who, it will be remembered, used to have their meals with him, as a favourite. Once so singled out, such an officer would then for a time play in Hess's mind the role of the emissary between himself and the alleged peace party in Britain. The patient would make the most naïve efforts to circumvent the security arrangements and scrutiny of his letters. It was a pity that his writings and the secret communiqués were not more interesting from the political intelligence point of view, from which angle childish irrational trust in his "favourite" was naturally encouraged. They contained only re-hashes of his familiar statements urging Britain to change her government and make peace while there was yet time.

To some extent the same pattern was repeated with regard to one of the six nursing orderlies to whom he would show special favours, and whom he would permit to do more for him than the others. This situation was exploited to extract from him a promise to his favourites that he would not, whilst they were in attendance, make further suicidal attempt. His fear of being poisoned was not to be dispelled by shifting the irksome duty of taking food with him from the officers to one of the medical orderlies who had in any case to be present. Hess argued that whilst his enemies would not scruple to sacrifice a mere lance-corporal in order to achieve their aim, they might hesitate before sending a member of His Majesty's bodyguard to his doom.

Provisional Conclusions.

It may be convenient at this point to insert some preliminary conclusions as they presented themselves after a month's intensive observation, but always with the handicap of the patient's refusal to give a consistent psychiatric history. On the whole, the mental symptoms which Hess showed formed a consistent picture. The combination of hypochondriacal symptoms, i.e. concern about his health and fear of some hidden internal weakness or malady (unsubstantiated by medical examination) on the one hand, and persecutory ideas about external enemies on the other hand, is of course well known, and places this patient's behaviour in the paranoid group of disorders. In addition he also displayed symptoms which would be generally agreed to fall more into the neurotic group; thus he was afraid of being passively conveyed in vehicles, and he showed some compulsive orderliness and ritualisation of his life, and marked conflict about indulgences of the palate. His secretiveness about his bowels was a notable feature.

These traits viewed together made it possible to venture on a diagnosis on psychological grounds. (The paranoid features of his personality were clearly seen in egocentricity, based on a deep feeling of insecurity, a fear of being injured and attacked. The psychological interpretation of such an attitude is that the patient has severe uncertainty and conflict about his own value and acceptance by society. He clearly has no great confidence in the goodness of other people, and while withdrawing in one sense into his "self" he is always looking for an idealised person outside himself whom he might love and trust in order to assuage his inner loneliness.) In this case the idealised person by and large was, of course, Hitler, but within the narrower pattern of life in his prison camp other men came to embody these opposing qualities. One by one he found them wanting and then identified them with the bad powers who were working against him. In a curious way, the gallant Duke of Hamilton and the chivalrous King of England were playing a role almost identical with Hitler as idealised objects of veneration in his mind. It might even be possible that Hess, finding the real Hitler ruthless and destructive, experienced great anxiety for the persistence of this (to him) so essential ideal, and turned towards the other Herrenvolk, i.e., the British, as an alternative saving symbol of the idea of goodness which was threatening to be overwhelmed by evil and destruction in his own personality. Hence, England must be saved.

At this stage it seemed fairly clear that Hess had acted on his own initiative and without the Fuehrer's consent in flying to Britain. He was somewhat tremulously hoping that the Fuehrer would understand his action of coming to England, implying that he had a deeper doubt of the perfect relationship between himself and Hitler of which he was so proud. In order to allay these doubts he had to delude himself that he was doing the will of the Fuehrer as he imagined him to be—a peace bringer. He could not, of course, admit or allow himself to know that he felt this doubt, and therefore in all his utterances he always rejected and denied any bad or aggressive qualities of his idol.

It is permissible also to speculate on the degree of guilt felt by Hess at the Fuehrer's aggressive behaviour towards the world, shown by such frequent remarks as: "How terrible to think of all the mothers mourning their sons and of the children behind their dead parents' coffins." Assailed by such degrees of guilt about aggressiveness, he could save his own mental integrity only by some dramatic act of redemption, which at the same time had the effect of removing him from Hitler's influence. This phase would, of course, correspond to the sense of grandeur and mission which paranoid individuals commonly display.

From the psychological point of view his attempt at "making peace" had failed, as it had also from the political standpoint. The bad impulses were not eliminated, for he found himself surrounded by a hostile prison regime. Instead of being hailed as the saviour of Britain and the world, he now became definitely persecuted, partly projecting his guilt over destructiveness into the notion of a hidden Jewish poisoner clique and partly increasing his hypochondriacal preoccupations with bad inside events in his stomach and liver, etc. As the day of the conference approached he felt himself more and more inadequate for his task, and deteriorated into a rather pitiful *malade imaginaire*.

The attempted suicide was probably very complexly motivated, as such attempts nearly always are. At the deepest level it was probably the expression of self-punishment urges at his own inadequacy in relation to the Messianic peace-bringer rôle which he had assumed. At the same time it was also no doubt an act of revenge against us for spurning him—a kind of

hara-kiri on the enemy's doorstep. His own expressed motiva-
tion, i.e., that he thereby wished to escape his inevitable
destruction at the hands of his enemies in the Jewish conspiracy,
would seem to have been an attempted rationalisation-
projection of his own inner destructive tendencies, but in line
with his persecutory delusions.

Lastly, he was acting to some extent in conformity with a
German cultural stereotype in which the "gentleman's code of
honour" prescribes suicide as the method of atoning for failure
to carry out a mission to the satisfaction of one's superiors, or
for losing face. We have the confirmatory example of scores of
suicides among high German military and political leaders who
behaved in a similar manner.

So far there was not much evidence to show whether this
paranoid system had been active in Hess before his arrival in
Great Britain.

A German of academic status who claimed to know Hess's
earlier behaviour, reported him to have been a sufferer from
"fits of depression over many years," and stated that he
"appeared to be a split personality."

In a letter to his wife, written in July, 1941, Hess, after
talking of his "self-imposed dieting," refers to the fact that
Reuther of Munich (a doctor of some kind) had got him to the
point where he could eat anything and no longer needed to take
precautions.

During this early phase of our observation the symptoms
would show considerable fluctuation in intensity, with large
tracts of reality well preserved and moments of insight. He was
not medico-legally insane and at this stage it seemed wiser to
label his condition as one of psychopathic personality of the
paranoid type—a label to which the physical evidence of
degeneration lent support. Here was a man of no mean
intellectual gifts, whose career had been that of the typically
unstable cranky drifter, common in Germany and also to be
found elsewhere among the demobilised ex-officer class of
World War I. One or two Germans have been encountered
who met Hess as a student at Munich, where he was a pathetic,
lonely, queer, but striking figure, dogging Professor Haushofer's
footsteps.

By way of providing a social background to his motives, it

may be interesting at this point to relate the essence of an interview which one of us had two years later with a German prisoner of war who had had an unusual opportunity of following the development of Hess's flight to England. This man was a journalist employed by the German broadcasting corporation, then subordinated to Goebbels's propaganda ministry. He was one of a number of men who took turns on a duty roster at the Central Information Bureau dealing with incoming messages. As is usual among such men, there was a great deal of unofficial gossip and "off the record" inside information swapped at this centre. This man, in the course of several long and apparently entirely frank conversations, told us that Hess had for a long time been losing influence among the German leadership. Hess owed his position entirely to his dog-like devotion to Hitler personally, but had been progressively excluded from policy-making, and was in fact functioning as a glorified head of Hitler's welfare department, dealing with hard luck appeals and all the more charitable aspects of the Nazi regime. Our informant, himself at one time a member of the Organisation of Germans Abroad, said he would have staked his life that Hess was opposed to using that organisation as a channel for espionage and fifth-column work. By so doing he had incurred the displeasure of Himmler especially, with whom Bohle (nominally Hess's deputy in that organisation) had ingratiated himself. Though nominally as the Fuehrer's deputy holding high rank in the S.S., Hess was in fact an opponent of its methods and aims. Behind the scenes there was a struggle for gaining control of that aspect of the Nazi Party's work which had to do with indoctrination and Party morale. In this aspect Hess was technically the leader, uneasily supported by Alfred Rosenberg. In point of fact, however, the S.S. set up its own school for doctrine and morale, the S.S. Kultur-Senat, with which Rosenberg, finding it the more powerful side, ultimately identified himself, leaving Hess without any actual power. Hess everywhere in Germany appeared to have maintained his reputation as a simple, un-selfseeking idealistic man, to whom people could appeal with hope of obtaining justice against grievances.

Our informant professed to know that there was something of a conspiracy led by the S.S. to isolate Hess from Hitler. He also

CHAPTER VI

MYTCHETT PLACE—PHASE TWO

In July, 1941, it was becoming clear that we were landed with the somewhat monotonous task of looking after an unstable prisoner for the duration of the war. Hess's knowledge of the English language was sufficiently good to make us feel that it was no longer necessary to have a German-speaking psychiatrist in charge of him; consequently on July 17th Major Dicks left to take up other work, and was replaced by Capt. Johnston, who had long experience of institutional care of psychiatric cases. Hess was confined to bed and was still under surgical treatment, and Capt. Johnston writes:

"On our first meeting, his attitude towards me was one of suspicion and correct formality. He appeared to be a sick man —gaunt, hollow-eyed and anxious.

"Throughout the early days of our association, I gradually succeeded in establishing a friendly relationship; he discussed his attempted suicide with me and claimed he had made the attempt because he felt he was going mad, and this was the best answer to his troubles. He strongly resented his confinement, but appreciated its necessity. He took an obvious pleasure in discussing his aeroplane trip to Scotland, and considered this was a very brave act, since he had had little practice of piloting planes since his experience as a lieutenant in the Air Force during the 1914-1918 war. He stated he made up his mind after the fall of France to visit this country, following a conversation with the Fuehrer, during which he became convinced that the latter really wished peace with England. He expressed satisfaction over the war with Russia, because he now felt that England would be more sympathetic towards Germany in her war against Communism. He still felt he would be able to bring about peace with England, when he recovered from his injury. We discussed Marshal Goering, and Hess showed one of his rare flashes of humour when I told him we laughed at Goering's many medals and uniforms, to which he replied: "So does Goering." His attitude towards the Fuehrer was obviously one of fanatical faith and loyalty, but he apparently disliked Goering and was jealous of his prestige in Germany. He remarked in rather a contemptuous manner that Goering would have been terrified at the thought of making the flight that he himself succeeded in doing when he flew to Scotland.

"As the days passed, it became evident that Hess was very much concerned with his own physical health—he was difficult with his food, and complained of many bodily aches and pains for which no organic basis could be found. He asked for camomile tea, which was procured for him, and for camomile enemata. He complained of insomnia, and although his sleep was much interrupted, the total amount was satisfactory. He was liable to long periods of moody self-absorption, and spent much time staring into the corner of the room, but refusing to discuss his thoughts. He was secretive and difficult to approach. During those early days he seemed upset by the absence of air-raid alerts and would say with great emphasis: 'They must come soon.'

"On the 28th July, 1941 his leg was X-rayed at the request of the surgical specialist. Hess had heard that X-rays rendered one sexually sterile, and he carefully used the lid of the sterilizer to cover his genitalia during exposures.

"A large part of his time was taken up with writing, and on August 2nd, 1941, he presented to one of the officers who was dining with him a lengthy statement in writing to be given to the father of this officer, who was a Member of Parliament. On translation the document was found to be the typical effusion of a paranoic, with its persecutory delusions and bizarre ideas of poisoning and torture. He did not accuse the other officers or myself of bad faith, but he believed that we were all under the influence of some rare poison or mesmerism, and that under this influence we were compelled to torture and poison him. The irrational nature of these accusations was quite lost on him."

At this time the consultant asked for a ruling from the authorities on the question of whether or no some of the physical methods of treatment, electric convulsant therapy or other techniques should be considered for the amelioration of Hess's condition. It was felt, however, after due consideration that his co-operation would be minimal and that should any minor

accident occur the complications would be considerable. For
this reason therefore nothing of this sort was done.

Dr. Johnston continues:

"He was liable to odd behaviour, such as lying with his
fingers in his ears and smiling to himself. When questioned
about this, he only replied: 'I am thinking.' He complained
frequently of the banging of doors, although this was not really
excessive in the house. He informed me that this was done
purposely to annoy and upset him, and on the banging of a
door he would fly into a rage.

"At this time Hess was working on grandiose plans for his
future dwelling-house. He said that he intended to build one in
Scotland, another in Sussex, and a third in Germany. The
accommodation in one of them provided for a dining-room for
180 persons.

"On September 5th, 1941, Hess was informed that a
Member of the Cabinet proposed to visit him; the effect of this
was very noticeable. During the next few days he became
moody, irritable and particularly sensitive to noises. He sent
for me complaining, for the first time, of severe cramps in the
abdomen, which apparently came on every few minutes. He
indulged in dramatic gestures, and gripped the Balkan Beam
supporting his leg, pulling himself up off the bed, and demanding
morphia. There did not appear to be any organic cause for this
disturbance, and the spasms ceased when his attention was
distracted. Immediately on my departure, he sent for the
Foreign Office representative and said he was too ill to undertake an important interview. He was visited by a Member of
the Cabinet (Lord Beaverbrook) on September 9th, and
conversed with him for an hour. He said afterwards that he had
enjoyed the conversation. On the following day he was much
more cheerful and made no further complaint of the abdominal
pain.

"During the next month he frequently complained of
constipation and occasional severe cramps. On September
27th he passed no urine all day and asked to be cathe-
terised. This was carried out and twenty-four ounces withdrawn.

"On October 2nd he sent for me and gave his word of
honour to make no attempt on his life if I would remove some

of the more irksome restrictions placed upon him, specifically the use of a knife to cut his meat and the use of a glass and a tea-cup of porcelain. This was granted on the understanding that I could withdraw these articles at any time I considered it advisable, such as when he was suffering pain or was emotion-ally upset. He passed the greater part of his days in reading, writing and listening to the wireless. On October 17th the surgical specialist allowed him to sit up in a chair for a short time each day.

"During the next few weeks he had periods when he was fairly cheerful and sociable, but he frequently became moody and depressed, staring at the walls smiling, grimacing and making no attempt to occupy himself.

"On November 14th he was moved from his bedroom to his sitting-room, which had been converted into a bed-sitting-room for the time being. This was done to enable us to fit armour-plated glass throughout his rooms and take other precautions against attempted suicide. As his fracture healed it was feared that the danger of suicide might again arise. The presence of the fracture had postponed the necessity to worry over the problem of his mission or justify his presence in this country.

"On November 21st Hess produced for the Foreign Office representative a bundle of papers wrapped around many times in tissue paper, and with his signature scribbled over it in every direction; he explained he had done this to prevent anyone tampering with the enclosures.

"About this time he was hiding odd pieces of paper about the room, under the couch, etc., and showed other evidences of delusions of persecution. He asked one of the medical orderlies to take charge of his secret papers, as he feared they would be read while he was asleep. He put them in a large envelope, sealed it with candle-grease, and used the signet ring of a medical orderly to stamp it. He complained of frequent headaches, nervousness and failing sight, and said he was sure these symptoms resulted from poisonous drugs given him in his food. He asked if the Foreign Office representative, the captain of the guard or myself would please have meals with him to ease his mind on this score. On the first occasion he had dinner with me, he was very gloomy and complained of loss of memory.

He said he was unable to converse because he could not remember words or what had happened even one hour previously. On December 4th he complained that his memory had completely gone and could never return. On December 8th he said that poison was being given him to prevent a meeting between himself and the Protecting Power, the Swiss Minister, and that by destroying his memory we would prevent him describing how we had persecuted and poisoned him. He withdrew his promise not to commit suicide. On January 12th, 1942, he was visited by the Swiss Minister and expressed satisfaction over the interview. On the day of this visit he ate no breakfast or lunch, and just prior to the interview he complained of confusion and loss of memory. These symptoms disappeared on the arrival of the minister, whom he kept in private conversation for three and a half hours. He wrote some lengthy documents, and gave the minister some tablets and the remains of a bottle of wine, in sealed bottles, which he asked to be analysed, partly in this country and partly in Switzerland, so that he could be sure they were not poisoned. On the day following the visit, Hess was much brighter and told me he had pretended to be confused and incapable of undertaking a serious interview, because he was sure we would have drugged him to prevent his telling the truth. He also asked to be provided with containers for faeces and urine so that he could have them analysed when he considered it necessary.

"He did not lose his fear of poison, however, and asked that all the meat should be served on one dish as a precaution. The fact that he ate his breakfast each morning alone did not seem to strike him as irrational. He continued to believe that noises inside and outside the house were specially arranged to upset him and were a subtle form of psychological torture. At this time he began to adopt a suspicious attitude towards the medical orderlies; he no longer chatted to them, and was abrupt and rude in ordering them about their duties. The slamming of doors was particularly irritating to him and on one occasion, when I was present, he suddenly strode over to the door of his room and slammed it with great violence, and stood laughing in a hysterical manner.

"On January 30th he complained that his wireless set was

being deliberately interfered with and refused reassurance on this point. He was liable at this time to short periods of confusion and frequently complained of loss of memory. This was more apparent than real, as he frequently forgot to act the part."

The comment in the report of the consultant at this time was as follows:

"Since my last visit the prisoner has made a good recovery from his physical injury, but mainly because of his abnormal ideas he has not been out of doors at all, having refused at all times to go. He looked to me a distinctly ill man, his face being more sunken and more grey, and in order to check up on this and to make sure that nothing at all was missed I asked for permission to have Lieut.-Colonel Evan Bedford come in from Cambridge Hospital to go over him physically. Colonel Bedford is a very distinguished consulting physician in civilian life and we could not possibly have a better opinion than his. Fortunately he finds that there is nothing fundamentally wrong* but considers that his poor condition is due to his lack of air and exercise and, of course, to his mental state.

"Hess's mental condition has deteriorated since I was last there. The delusional, persecutory ideas have evidently fallen into the background for the moment, but, as often happens, he has swung into a depression and with it a distinct loss of memory. This may be due to the increasing mental deterioration or it may be just a phase from which he will emerge. His memory was very much at fault. He did not remember that he had received any letters at all from his wife. He cannot remember, and it was obviously quite genuine, that he had had a visit from the Protecting Power. He talked to me in disjointed, rather monosyllabic fashion, but I gather that he will for some days at a time sit moodily saying nothing to anyone."

Dr. Johnston's account continues:

"On March 27th it was found that he had been secreting a few tablets of glucose and luminal. These tablets were in the lining of his flying boots and under the carpet, and he explained his behaviour by saying he was sure they were poisonous, and he intended to give them to the Swiss Minister.

* Pulse 80. B.P. 125/70. Short squeaky systolic murmur at the apex noticed by the medical officer from the start which is of no significance.

He was complaining almost daily of severe abdominal cramps which he dramatised by striding up and down the room, writhing and groaning in a ridiculous manner. The object of this behaviour was apparently to demonstrate to us the terrible effects of the poisons we were supposed to be administering to him."

Dr. Rees in his report of April 20th said:

"I paid a further visit to Camp Z on Saturday last, April 18th. Hess was in bed but very talkative and quite different to his state at my last visit, when he was very depressed and shut away. No doubt his condition on Saturday was due to the fact that he was expecting a visit from the Protecting Power in the immediate future. He complained of a violent headache: 'The worst I have ever had in my life,' but he refused to take some aspirin I gave him out of my pocket even though I gave him his choice of tablets and took the others myself. He told me that he was quite certain that he was being poisoned, and he was very emphatic in his criticism of the authorities for leaving him where he now is when he had asked for removal six months ago!

"H.E. the Swiss Minister arrived shortly afterwards and most devotedly spent three hours with Hess. There was no question whatever in his mind, of course, of the mental derangement, and a good deal of the time was occupied apparently by a careful wrapping up and labelling of various tablets of glucose, luminal, aspirin, etc., and samples of claret, all of which were to be investigated. Hess has apparently refused to touch the Red Cross parcels which have come for him from Germany, since they have passed through Switzerland and might have been poisoned there, as he said: "I have many enemies in Switzerland." This is an important confirmatory point in demonstrating his delusional symptom to anyone who may in future doubt it, since these parcels reached him with the seals unbroken and the Berlin post-mark on them."

Dr. Johnston concludes:

"During the next few months, Hess showed little change in his outlook and behaviour. He retained his delusions regarding poisoning and still accused us of torturing him by creating noises.

"On June 6th Brigadier Rees visited him, and told him

that arrangements were being made to transfer him to a quieter area, in Wales. He was very sceptical about this and refused to believe it. On June 25th, 1942, he was taken by car to his new quarters; he showed a childish pleasure in the journey. He was introduced to Major Ellis Jones, in whose care I left him.

"There is the picture: I have made no attempt to interpret or explain it, but it is one that is only too familiar to the mental hospital doctor. The anxious, gloomy paranoiac, with a mind strangled and warped by the ever-encroaching tentacles of his own persecutory delusions, until every thought and action minister only to delusional ends."

CHAPTER VII

IT would be hard to avoid repetition if one attempted to give the day to day history of over three years' stay in this one hospital. It seems best, therefore, to begin this chapter with a condensed picture of the whole phase prepared by those psychiatrists who were in daily touch with Hess throughout the period. Following that are some amplifications of specific points.

A summary of the medical record of Hess while at Maindiff, prepared by Dr. Ellis Jones and Dr. Phillips.

It is perhaps desirable to state why Maindiff Court was chosen as the hospital to receive this patient. The choice was not haphazard but was determined by two main principles:

1. That the hospital was suitable for the accommodation of a psychopathic personality, but not one where mental cases were being treated.
2. That it should be a hospital where officers and Service patients of other ranks were actually undergoing treatment.

Maindiff Court fulfilled these requirements as, though it was normally the Admission Hospital of the County Mental Hospital situated about one and a half miles distant, it was used for five years under the Emergency Medical Service scheme for the treatment of Service patients, with one villa set aside for the treatment of officers, and no mental patients were under treatment there.

Condition of Admission.

Admitted June 25th, 1942. A tall, well-built man, pale and rather thin following a long period of indoor confinement as a result of his refusal to take outdoor exercise. His general physical state was good and there was no obvious disability

67

following a fracture of the leg he had sustained whilst at
Mytchett. Mentally he was alert and his reaction to his new
quarters was that of a normal individual; he was interested and
apparently pleased with the change of surroundings, but his
bearing was suspicious.

Progress of the Case.

Whilst dining with him that evening, he remarked that he
was anxious to get rid of his "fixed ideas", i.e. delusion about his
food being poisoned. On the morning of the 26th and 27th he
stated that he had slept fairly well, but complained of noise of
the trains keeping him awake. During the months of July and
August his manner and conversation were that of a normal
individual. He occupied himself in intensive reading, especially
at this time being engrossed in Lloyd George's *History of The
World War*, in redesigning his proposed house—a combination
of an official and a private residence. He went out in the car for
short runs into the country, and was encouraged to exercise as
much as possible. His condition was such that the account
given of his mental state at Mytchett was almost incredible. On
September 25th he was informed that Brigadier Rees would
visit him; to my surprise on the morning of the 26th he had the
wild look described by Captain Johnston, and at the same time
he revealed a complete psychotic picture of paranoid reaction.
He stated that he was being poisoned, that Maindiff had been
specially chosen because of the proximity of the railway line, so
that the noise would annoy him, and that his wireless set was
being interfered with. During that evening the presence of
auditory hallucinations was noted; he kept looking behind and
ultimately turned around to stare at the surrounding bushes,
but he denied the presence of auditory hallucinations when
questioned.

He became increasingly irritable, adopted various devices
not to take the obvious piece of meat or vegetable that was his
portion with the officer he was dining with. Frequently he used
to ask one of us to eat a portion of his food also. Accompanying
this phase was the increasing number of attacks of what
became known amongst his associates as "abdominal cramps".
He would roll on the floor, make peculiar noises as if in great
pain and cry out for a hot-water bottle—later lie in a state of

extreme exhaustion. When, owing to the shortage of rubber, no replacement of the bottle could be obtained, he was satisfied with a medicine-bottle filled with warm water, which he used to place on his abdomen!

During this period, owing to his suspicious attitude, many amusing situations arose—I remember on one occasion we decided to have a picnic and asked him whether he would care to join us. He refused, but immediately we were in the car asked one of us to obtain a bottle of lemonade—this was procured with some difficulty. At tea, he, childlike, refused to participate until the others had gone to the summit of a hill to see the view; then he devoured all that was left of the sandwiches, etc.

To return to the "cramps", these were definitely associated with his delusions of poisoning, for he believed that they were caused by poison which was placed in his food. Later his delusions became less prominent, and he again became more sociable, but with increasing depression, marked hypochondriasis and complaints of intense fatigue.

Fortunately for those in authority, this retreating of his paranoid state was a blessing; because if it had persisted and his conduct had become more difficult, the question of his transfer to a mental hospital might have had to be considered. This alternation of "tension from without" and "tension from within" continued unabated, except for short periods when he reached a high degree of normality, until October, 1943, when he began to show an unusual phase in a case of paranoia and developed an amnesia.

The onset was gradual, but it was progressive and marked; he could give little account of his past life, forgot about the prominent part he played in the formation of the Nazi Party; he could not remember his schooldays in Germany or his childhood in Alexandria. His great difficulty was a failure in the process of recall, and he became apparently genuinely distressed by this. He forgot anybody who was only an occasional visitor, even his nursing orderlies after they had been away for a short period of leave. A state such as this was a very unusual feature in a paranoiac, but it was agreed that the condition was psychogenic and not organic. The mechanism of this amnesia led to considerable discussion as to whether it was hysterical or

malingering. The general opinion was that the condition was of
an hysterical nature but that memory was not far beyond the
effort of voluntary recall.

Simple persuasion having failed, permission was obtained
from the War Office to make an attempt, during the injection of
intravenous pentothal, to elicit the complete psychological
setting of the symptom. This was done in the presence of
Lieut.-Col. H. V. Dicks, who speaks German fluently. The full
report on this procedure, made at this time, is reproduced on a
later page. The attempt failed, and although permission was
given for further injections the patient refused to co-operate.
The state of amnesia continued until *February 4th, 1945*, when
he rose earlier than usual, was noted to be very agitated and
asked to see one of us (D. E. J.). First of all he said that his
memory had returned, and that he had something important to
tell the world, and he asked that the information he was about to
give should be forwarded to the Prime Minister. He produced
a sheet of paper on which were written the following names:

1. King of Italy and Marshal Badoglio.
2. Names of the Germans who threw a bomb at the Fuehrer.
3. Mr. Winston Churchill.
4. General Von Paulus.
5. Rudolf Hess.
6. Mr. Anthony Eden.
7. General J.
8. One of us (D. E. J.).
9. Brigadier J. R. Rees.
10. The Bulgarian Government, etc.

He stated that the Jews had "some power" to hypnotise
people without their being aware of any change in their
personality, and that in this hypnotic state they did their
misdeeds. All the above people mentioned had been thus
hypnotised and he proceeded to enlarge about each of the
names in the following way:

1. Neither of these would have concluded an armistice with
   the Allies after giving their word to the Fuehrer unless
   they had been thus "hypnotised"
2. Similar action on these Germans.
3. Hypnosis explains his change of attitude from being
   anti-Bolshevik to pro-Russian.

4. The explanation for his reported broadcasts from Russia.
5. The explanation for his own rudeness to the collaborators in Italy at a State banquet when obviously it was imprudent to have displayed this.
6. Mr. Eden had on one occasion been rude to Goering at a State banquet; obviously he had been affected by this hypnosis.
7. General J.—he had been rude to the patient at Mytchett; again he could only have done so under the effect of hypnosis.
8. One of us (D. E. J.) was under the effect of the same spell, and as a result, though he did not know it, he had been the means whereby poison was placed in his food; that this poison was the cause of the pains in his abdomen and of his neuralgia.
9. The explanation of his manner to the patient at one of his visits.
10. The reason for the change of attitude of the Bulgarian Government.

During the afternoon of this day he asked for a bread-knife; saying he wished to make some toast, he went into his bedroom, changed into his Air Force uniform and then came back to his sitting-room, where he stabbed himself in the left lower chest (6th intercostal space). He maintained that the knife had been pushed in up to the hilt (about 8 inches) but his general and local condition did not support this. Two stitches only were inserted in the wound, and he was given sodium luminal intramuscularly. In an agitated state he maintained that his amnesia had been simulated.

February 5th. He gave two reasons for attempting suicide:
1. That he would never be allowed to leave this country.
2. That he could see it was all over with Germany, that it would be overrun by the Bolshevisks, that the Russians would reach the English Channel and proceed to Bolshevise this country.

February 6th. He weaved the attempt at suicide into his delusional state in this way—the knife was placed there by the Jews to tempt him to commit suicide because he was the only person who knew of their secret power of hypnosis. He continued to refuse all food but he drank water freely if it had been tasted by one of us.

February 8th. Refuses to be shaved, and says he has decided to grow a beard. Is still taking no food, and he says he has decided to starve himself to death. On this subject he maintains that in Germany a person who believes himself to be incurable can, of his own free will and accord, end his life. He had therefore made a signed declaration to the British and German Governments of his desire to die as he considers that his abdominal condition is incurable. He wishes his corpse to be dressed in his flying uniform and to be sent to Germany, where on examination poison will obviously be found.

February 12th. Having been without food since the 4th instant, though taking water freely, it was agreed to use forcible feeding. When he saw that we were determined to proceed with the feeding he protested vigorously, but stated that he would take some orange juice, which he did, and promised to take some milk the next day. From this time onward he took all nourishment satisfactorily. As his condition improved he stated that the attempt on his life was not a real one, and that he had deliberately chosen the *6th* intercostal space. This statement was contrary to that given when he first gave the reason for his attempt at suicide, and shows a degree of (confabulation.) During this period of refusal of food there were no attacks of abdominal cramps—his logical sequence being: no food, no poison, hence no cramps.

From late February he again took a keen interest in the daily news, but fortunately for us and himself all the catastrophes arising on the continent were weaved into his delusional state, for example the capture of the Remagen Bridgehead was explained in this way—that the soldiers who were guarding the bridge had been hypnotised by the Jews. He constantly referred to the great danger of Communism overrunning Europe and ultimately Britain. He occupied his time with reading and preparing his defence at the trial which it was then reported would take place. The defence was simply a repetition of the now well known Nazi doctrine. During this period he was confined in a room twenty-four feet by sixteen feet, with a nursing orderly constantly in attendance. To detach himself from the presence of the orderly he used to read constantly, and it was this attitude that he found so easy to adopt in the dock at Nuremberg, showing an apparent indifference to the proceedings.

In July, 1945, he again complained of loss of memory, grotesque in its nature, but close observation revealed that there was a much greater degree of conscious simulation than previously. Lt. P. C. Fenton, M.B.E., and one of us (D. E. J.) agreed that we would not accept his plea of loss of memory; the other officers accepted the loss, with the result that the latter complained what a dull personality he was. D. E. J. mentioned to him several times that, if asked in a court of law to give evidence, he would state that his memory was quite normal. This never evinced a word of protest (unlike the person suffering from hysterical amnesia). We would deliberately forget to obtain certain necessaries; he never forgot to remind us. A classical example of his ability to remember what he wished was at the time of the trial of William Joyce. The report of this case was very fully reported in *The Times* and he remarked to us how very interesting these arguments had been, and he was pleased to think that the charges would be dismissed. (At one time, with the judge dismissing one indictment after the other, it seemed that this would be the case.) I immediately asked him: "You remember all about Joyce then?" his answer was: "Yes," and he remembered that he was called Lord Haw-Haw in this country. This different attitude with Lt. Fenton and one of us was frequently commented upon.

Again (wrote Dr. Jones), my daughter was preparing to go away to a boarding school, and I was discussing this with him when he asked: "What are you going to do with the pony?" He knew previously that she had a pony. Another example of his ability to remember when he wished to was on the morning of his departure. I was anxious that certain articles which belonged to the hospital were not taken away by him—he agreed with my keeping these, and I was under the impression that a grey dressing-gown he had was the property of the hospital; he denied this, and stated he had brought it with him to this hospital. Again, hanging on the wall of his room were various photographs of his wife and child; above these was that of the Fuehrer. He took with him all of these except that of the Fuehrer. If, as he maintained in Nuremberg, he could not remember about his family, how did he know these were photographs of them, and that he had a personal interest in them?

On arrival at Nuremberg, the colonel in charge of the party asked him in what direction the city was situated—he stated he did not know. Later whilst he was standing on the airfield awaiting transport, I asked him the same question—he pointed it out to one of us (D. E. J.). These incidents and his general manner so different from that of his previous amnesia led the nursing orderlies, and the others in immediate contact, to conclude that there was a very considerable degree of conscious simulation.

On October 6th, 1945, orders were received that the patient was to be taken to Nuremberg on October 8th. Knowing the patient's obstinacy and refusal to co-operate if informed beforehand of any event, he was not informed of his impending departure until early in the morning of the day chosen. After considerable persuasion he packed his cases and made a rather inglorious exit, having lost all of his former haughty manner. He was flown from Madley, near Hereford, to Brussels, where a short stay was made for lunch, and then on to Nuremberg, where he was handed over to the American authorities and placed in the old gaol of the ancient city.

Some of the details of the picture drawn above can be filled in now by a limited number of extracts taken from the lengthy periodic reports rendered by the consulting psychiatrist after his visits.

August 4th, 1942.

"Mentally he is markedly better for the moment. He has even got to the point of talking about his delusional ideas, and saying that he hopes they will not recur and that he is practically convinced they were delusions.

"This improvement in Hess's condition coincides partly with what he considers to be a great improvement in the war news from his angle."

September 29th 1942.

"—he has gone back again and become more difficult. Yesterday he was very tense and strained, rather dramatic in his manner and clearly depressed. I am told that this is his most common mood nowadays in the mornings (and I saw him at 10.30 a.m.). He told me that the Swiss Minister had taken away various specimens of wines, medicines, etc. from Mytchett and that on his last visit to Maindiff he had reported that all the analyses were perfectly clear. I asked him whether that had really satisfied him that there was no attempted poisoning and he said yes, but that he still felt from time to time that there was this risk and for a while believed it.

"He has apparently been very obsessed by the noise of the trains shunting at the neighbouring station, but during the last three weeks, since the fighting at Stalingrad got difficult, he has been having his abdominal cramps again, and is less worried by the noise. The situation therefore is very much as I have reported in earlier notes to you. He is a paranoid person of a psychopathic type who has definite hysterical and hypo-chondriacal tendencies. Like all people who have a similar make-up, he reacts to circumstances and is likely to be worried when they are difficult and better when things are going well. There is still the risk of further attempted suicide, especially at times when he is tense and hunted, as he is again to some extent now.

"The patient has no grumbles of any material kind. He would, I think, quite like to be somewhere different but that need not be taken seriously. He would also, I think, welcome company provided it was somebody whom he regarded as sufficiently important."

From the point of view of reassuring his wife about his state of health it was arranged that there should be a careful physical examination carried out, and Major-General Arnold Stott went down with Brigadier Rees to see him. Appended to the signatures of the report were the civil life appointments of the two physicians concerned, put in to reassure the patient and his relations or their own doctors in Germany.

November 6th, 1942.

A long summary of the whole case had been prepared for the Lord Privy Seal from which a report could be prepared for the Soviet Government. The last paragraph of the conclusions ran:

"From the angle of 'responsibility' it is in my opinion doubtful whether at any time he has been prevented by his mental difficulties from knowing the nature and quality of his acts."

January 14th, 1943.

Major Ellis Jones reported as follows:

"I beg to submit a report on 'J' since your last visit on 26.10.42. Following his examination by Major-General Stott, for a few days he was reassured as to his bodily health, but he soon relapsed into a depressed and hypochondriacal state; accompanying this affective state delusions of persecution and interference have been prominent. The delusions have been many and varied, the prominent ones being: interference with his wireless set, interference with his food and his personal property, especially his socks. Up until the 2nd week of December his mental state continued as stated; he was so engrossed in his delusions and hallucinations (the presence of which I have repeatedly observed) that he was not interested in the news, books etc., except the book by T. 122 (Commander Grenfell) on naval strategy. During this period the only exercise he took was walking in the court-yard morning and evening with myself. He became convinced that he had heart disease. All types of medicine (including belladonna) have been tried for his 'cramps' but I am convinced that he does not take any of them, being too suspicious about all of them. Later he concentrated his delusional state on the evacuation of his bowels, imagining that something was given him to prevent them being opened, and asked me to promise to be present at his post-mortem and to keep the contents of the bowels for examination by the International Commission. During this period he was examined by the command ophthalmologist assisted by the district ophthalmologist. The glasses ordered were received—they were exactly similar to the ones ordered for him at his previous residence. The real reason why he wished to be examined was—with one eye certain distant objects appear double and he had weaved this into his delusional state. (He wears neither pair of spectacles.)

"He has had massage for his leg from Male Nurse Clifford during the past few weeks. The only question to discuss about his medical state is whether a complete Barium follow-through should be done. I fear that he would not co-operate—the one occasion I mentioned same he decidedly refused to consider it.

"During the 2nd week in Dec. he was persuaded to go out in order that a power plug could be fixed in his bedroom. Lt. M. persevered and persuaded him to go out; following this and up to the present he has had frequent country walks. Co-incident with this re-commencement of his country rambles there has been a change in his affective state from one of depression and dejection to one of mild elation with renewed interest in his personal appearance (even to a request for hair cream), congenial conversation and an interest in books, etc., with a consequent diminution in the prominence of his delusions.

"There is one important point which is constantly uppermost in my mind, the one of suicide. I feel that stringent and adequate precautions would make his life unbearable, increase the prominence of his delusions and accelerate his deterioration, and that if he was determined to commit suicide, he is so intelligent and secretive that he would outwit us all and that adequate precautions would accentuate any desire for suicide."

May 21st, 1943.

This report was made just after the notable successes of the 8th Army in North Africa and the forward move in Tunisia.

"For the first time in all my visits he refused to shake hands nor did he rise from his chair to greet me. He said that he had decided that until after the war he was not going to shake hands with anyone. That presumably is part of his reaction to what he clearly recognises as bad news although he explains away to himself the news and firmly declares to the officers of guard and to Major Ellis Jones that he really accepts all the Goebbels broadcasts. His abdominal pains, which I have said previously are functional and not organic in origin, are noticeably worse at times when the news is bad. This is what one would expect.

"—Though he did not express this to me, I am told by Major Ellis Jones that he still at times talks as though he would resume his position as Deputy when he returns to Germany. He en-quired whether I had met Von Arnim or Von Thoma, which made me wonder whether he missed companionship or would like to have anybody else with him. He said no, that it was better that he should be by himself——"

August 4th, 1943.

"—evidence of further deterioration in the patient's condition——"

October 7th, 1943.

The patient had improved.

"He was more talkative and friendly . . ."

February 3rd, 1943.

The amnesic symptoms had begun.

"—Although on my last visit on October 5th, 1943 he was better, it might have been possible that a gradual deterioration of his mental condition would lead to an organic loss of memory, though such conditions are very rare and do not as a rule come about in such a short time. That, however, can be excluded, and the absence of any physical signs of disease confirms this.

"His condition is therefore an hysterical amnesia, very comparable to the state which is developed by many soldiers in war-time, and by not a few civilians in peace-time when confronted by situations which they feel it is impossible to face. A loss of memory is in these cases a self-protective mechanism. Apparently, the prisoner's amnesia began rather gradually soon after my last visit, and it seems to have coincided with the increasing seriousness of the war news from the Russian front, and at the same time with his greater self-absorption owing to the cutting off of his expeditions outside the hospital.

"With regard to treatment, if the prisoner were an ordinary civilian wanting treatment and ready to be co-operative, it is practically certain that we could recover the whole of his memory in a very short time either by the use of hypnosis or by what is called narco-analysis, i.e., by the use of an anæsthetic drug given intravenously. Unfortunately, even if it were thought justifiable to use hypnosis, he would be very resistant to that and some objection has previously been raised by the Foreign Office to the use of drugs, which I suppose still holds—

"It is interesting that as the amnesia developed, the paranoid ideas of poisoning retreated into the background and have hardly been expressed for many weeks. The day before my visit they had revived or come to the fore again, and I think that probably, if they do, that will mean that the hysterical amnesia will recede, i.e., I think that it is a good sign from the 'political' angle that the delusional system is coming to the fore again. Apart from his abdominal 'cramps' he is well, there are no complaints about his sleep and his agitation was not much in evidence."

January 21st, 1944.

Hess had written a letter to his wife which refers to the loss of memory. A translation of that letter may be of interest:

"England (21.1.44).

"DEAR LITTLE MUMMY,

"I have been sitting down, literally for hours, considering what I shall write to you, and I get no further. Unfortunately there is a special reason for it. As, sooner or later, you will notice it and hear about it, I am writing to you about it. I have completely lost my memory; all the past fades away as behind a grey fog; I can no longer remember even the most obvious things. I do not know the cause. The doctor gave me a long explanation but even that in the meantime has vanished away from my memory. He promises, however, that everything will be all right again some day. I hope he is right.

"But that is the reason why I cannot, in fact, write you a reasonable letter; for that purpose one wants a memory more than one believes. It is another matter when one has letters to answer which supply one with material and suggestions, but I received your last letter on 13th September of last year! I am therefore waiting and I shall only write to you again when I receive post from you again; some day that will be the case again.

"Two letters arrived from Aunt Emma recently so that I heard at least that all was well with you, at any rate at the beginning of December—touch wood!

"Please send me again some books. In the monotony of my solitary imprisonment they are of the greatest value to me.

"Greetings to all and especially loving ones to you and the boy.

"Heil Hitler!
"Your,
"GR."

March 3rd, 1944.

The report made by Lt.-Col. Dicks to the consulting psychiatrist on a visit made especially to try and make use of narco-analysis is quoted here in full:

Object of Visit.

1. Acting on your verbal instructions, I proceeded to Maindiff Court, Mon., arriving 2100 hrs. 26th Feb. owing to lateness of trains. The object of my visit was to enable us to understand the patient's utterances in German, should he consent to an injection of (Evipan) for the relief of his present disorder of memory. It was also felt that my previous acquaintance with the case might be valuable in assessing the clinical state of the patient and reactions which might result from the proposed treatment. I considered it important not to appear to be the prime mover in suggesting the treatment, and therefore decided to subordinate myself to Major Ellis Jones, in clinical charge of the patient.

Approach to Patient.

2. Before seeing the patient, Ellis Jones and I decided on a plan of action. Ellis Jones was going to introduce me as a German speaker, and as the doctor who had looked after him earlier, with the avowed purpose of helping him to remember past incidents. When this had been done, and if the patient had found himself unable to recall these experiences, he was going to put the suggestion of possible help to him, with me backing him up. As anticipated, the patient showed no signs of recognising me, but seemed delighted to find someone with whom he could converse in his own tongue. Ellis Jones, in my presence, obtained a spontaneous expression of the patient's sense of "despair" at his inability to remember familiar names and even recent events. The idea of curability was duly introduced and amplified with examples of other cases successfully treated. We thought it wise to state that the best treatment was an injection. It was not at this stage proposed that the patient himself should undergo the treatment. The idea was left for him to assimilate.

Impressions of Patient's Clinical Condition.

3. In the meantime I had the opportunity of a long friendly chat with him, and of observing his condition, as compared with the summer of 1941. The physical state seemed good. The expression has become more fixed and dull and unhappy.

4. There was no evidence of any paranoid symptoms, e.g., fear of being poisoned, or even of suspicion. He opened up with evident pleasure to me and liked hearing about his past in a talk during which I reminded him of the salient features of his life and career. He laughed with amused incredulity at the idea that he could ever have been close to Hitler, jumped with a parachute or lived in Egypt. He obviously relished my flattery of his past powers, intended to make him wish for restoration of his full mental capacity.

5. The memory gap is a typical hysterical symptom. There is very little true distress about it. From time to time he asks one to define a simple notion like "ski-ing" or who Shakespeare was, but accepts definitions by other terms which should, by rights, be equally obscure. Attention and concentration are well maintained when desired. He describes his mental state as one in which events and ideas gradually slip into a fog, so that he can only remember the immediately preceding twenty-four hours of his life. It is a constriction of the field of consciousness in so far as it depends on past relationships, associations and references. Within this field, vocabulary is full and meaningful, and ideation and judgment unimpaired and rapid. There is some instability of mood from humour to petulance. Those who look after him agree that management has become much easier since his present phase began.

6. He eats greedily and rapidly, but tends to feel guilty about it. He suffered from an attack of abdominal pain during my presence, heavily dramatised. When relief by a tablet was suggested, he quickly slipped in his aversion to any form of medicinal treatment—"and that, of course, would include an injection". He was anxious to discover whether he had always shown this dislike, which he could not understand. Here was obviously a first reaction to the idea of Evipan.

7. In the course of these observations I concluded that while the symptoms of memory loss are genuine, i.e., not consciously simulated, they are of a superficial character, recalling the

described cases of Ganser syndrome and hysterical pseudo-dementia. In Henderson and Gillespie's *Textbook* an association of such symptoms with paranoid schizophrenia is described.

Reaction to Proposed (Evipan Treatment.)

8. The behaviour of the patient in the course of the following day (28th Feb.) was interesting. His early mental reservation has already been noted in paragraph 6. The following day Major Ellis Jones and I visited him during the short interval between his morning toilet and lunch. He showed some suspicion and "cold-shouldering" towards me. In the afternoon, during a long talk with both of us, Ellis Jones made a definite proposal of treatment for his memory (a trolley had been prepared to carry out the procedure in case he agreed). The patient pleaded that he would prefer "mental training". When Ellis Jones replied that this would not be effective in his case, the patient made the following very significant remark which I reproduce as nearly verbatim as possible:

"My present condition is good enough while I am a prisoner. I have had it for some time now. It doesn't really matter whether I can remember what I have done before. So long as I can read, draw and amuse myself somehow to kill time, I am satisfied. I do not suffer unless I am reminded of my disability. When I get back to Germany perhaps it will pass, or I can find some treatment. Perhaps it is even a merciful dispensation of fate which makes me forget. If I got back my full memory I might suffer more. So I prefer to wait and see."

At the end of this statement he burst into cheerful laughter, and was in high spirits for the rest of the day.

This piece of psychological insight augured ill for the success of the plan. He was invited by Ellis Jones to ponder the matter for twenty-four hours, if not in his own interest, then at least for the sake of his relatives, who must have felt worried by the letter he had sent his wife, and by the scarcity of his news, attributable to his condition. We were there to help him and he had nothing to fear. Here the matter was left. A telephonic report was made to Brigadier Rees.

9. On the next day (29th Feb.) the patient was in a bad humour, and occupied our attention with a number of trifling

complaints and grievances against his attendants. One felt this was done in order to hold the initiative and to resist suggestion. Reminded by Major Ellis Jones of his need for treatment, the patient stated categorically and clearly that his mind was made up to wait for a natural cure, and to refuse any artificial treatment involving the use of drugs.

10. During the afternoon I thought it wise to accompany him and the military duty officer (Lt. Fenton, P.C.) on a country walk. Normally, Lt. Fenton enjoys the patient's confidence, and these walks are the occasion for a good deal of friendly talk and enjoyment of natural beauty. On this occasion Lt. Fenton saw a great difference, which was also clear to me. The patient was taciturn, the atmosphere tense and suspicious, and the walk curtailed at his request.

11. In the course of the day the patient had written a fresh letter to his wife, and, contrary to his invariable practice, had sealed down the envelope. All present inferred that this was a reaction to the presence of a German-speaking officer in the camp, i.e., myself. I decided that no further useful purpose was served by my stay, which might indeed involve Major Ellis Jones in suspicion. I took brief and formal leave of the patient, and he professed blandly to be sorry I could not stay.

Possible Future Steps.

12. It is unlikely that this patient, with his long-established persecutory system about poisoning, will consent to what must seem to him a "chemical assault" on his body. Should he do so, in the absence of the suspicious stranger (myself), I suggest that someone with knowledge of German, not necessarily myself, be despatched to Maindiff, by fast car if need be. This interpreter should only be present in the room during the stage of narcosis and not enter into the patient's ken at all. Any notes made should be worked through by Dr. Ellis Jones, whom the patient trusts. The suggestion for treatment might most suitably be revived by a non-medical confidant, e.g., Lt. Fenton.

13. Some form of suggestion therapy, as by the use of an electrical or light apparatus, might be tried. I regard the patient as too intelligent to be amenable to this, and his under-lying paranoid system would also be likely to prevent a sufficient trust in the doctor for the procedure to succeed. An inducement

D

to submit to treatment might be the prospect of some reward or tangible disadvantages, e.g., loss of exercise, etc., related to the persistence of the present symptoms.

14. The symptom of memory loss has high protective value to the patient, as shown in paragraph 8. Whether its motives include a wish to be repatriated is an open question. The condition is sufficiently explained by the relief afforded him from mental anxiety and tension, due both to inner delusions and to the impact of war news. From the clinical point of view his state now is much easier and more manageable, to himself and others. I am therefore pessimistic as to the success of any treatment aimed at the removal of this, to him, "merciful dispensation of fate".

April 27th, 1944.

Major Ellis Jones wrote:

"Yesterday the patient was out and he failed to remember that he had visited a certain castle on previous occasions. This morning he was distressed about this and asked: 'Couldn't something be done about it?' I replied that there was a possibility of 'recovering his memory' by the use of an injection. This afternoon he asked to see me, and stated that he was willing to submit to the treatment.

"Owing to the probability of his native language being used during treatment I feel it would be advisable for Col. Dicks to be present during the treatment.

"Of course he may again refuse to co-operate but the above is the present position."

It seems significant from the point of view of the "genuineness" of the hysterical loss of memory that the patient should himself have been so worried at a failure to remember ordinary day to day details that he should ask for treatment and consent to the injection of the drug he had always feared.

What followed is best set out by reproducing Col. Dicks's report:

May 10th, 1944

"Acting on your verbal instructions, I paid a second visit to Maindiff Court, arriving on May 6th at 1830 hours.

"*Object of Visit:* The patient having consented to treatment for restoration of his memory by Evipan narcosis, it was to be my role to talk, and listen to his utterances, in German, in case he was unable to use English in the post-narcotic state of mind.

"A conference was held on the evening of May 6th between Dr. Phillips, Major Ellis Jones, R.A.M.C., and myself. It was decided to conceal my presence until the Evipan had taken effect. The reasons were: (a) that my appearance before the treatment might re-activate subconscious resistance owing to his associations with my personality dating back to an acute phase of paranoid excitement and suspicion; and (b) that there might be a possible beneficial 'shock' effect if he found himself addressed unexpectedly in his native tongue during the post-narcotic period.

The Treatment: "At the patient's request the treatment took place at about 2100 hours on Sunday, May 7th. This was to enable him to remain in bed after it was over in case he wished to go to sleep.

"Major Ellis Jones administered intravenous Evipan at 2100 hours in the presence of Dr. Phillips and a sergeant and corporal of the R.A.M.C. I entered the room when narcosis had supervened. The injection and course of treatment proceeded very normally, without untoward effect. During the post-narcotic (i.e., the psychiatrically important) phase he received first some suggestion from me, in German, that he would now be able to remember all that he had forgotten and be healed of his mental affliction. At first, I, and subsequently, Major Ellis Jones, put a large number of stimulus questions covering all the significant persons and episodes in the patient's life. It was noted by us that in response to some of these a look of recognition came into his features. His replies, however, mainly took the form of groans, complaints of abdominal pain or of thirst, and at a later stage of echo-like repetition of the question as put to him. The effective stage came to an end at 2215 hours, when the patient requested food and drink. A full, in parts verbatim, report of the session is appended, which gives psychiatric and technical details.

After-Effects: "The patient was seen first by Major Ellis Jones, and subsequently by me, at 2330 hours. He looked cheerful. Major Jones had told him we had now been able to convince ourselves that his memory was intact, that he had been able to remember quite a number of things, but that there had not been the full restoration of memory sometimes achieved in a single session.

"The patient expressed his gratitude for what had been done, stated he felt comforted and reassured by our remarks that no serious or irremediable defect existed in his memory function, but unfortunately his mind was just as 'blank' now as it had been. He was settled down for the night. which passed un-eventfully.

"A further conference was held by the three physicians present, at which we concluded that, in the light of experience and of the course of the treatment in this case, the result must be regarded as therapeutically negative, and any further sessions likely to meet with stronger mental resistance.

Subsequent Steps Taken: "The patient was seen the next day, May 8th, on rising. He complained of 'muzziness' in the head and abdominal discomfort. It was put to him both by Ellis Jones and by myself that further Evipan treatment might finally overcome his memory defect. We both met with his old dread of having foreign substances introduced into his system, and his statements that only absolute necessity would cause him to overcome his strong reluctance to have more Evipan.

"Major Jones followed up this cue later, dwelling on the sorrow he was causing his wife, the need to have his faculties in working order, etc. Later, during a long and quite friendly conversation, I reiterated these points, and also appealed to his vanity by such arguments as that a man of his importance and gifts should in his own interest do all he could to keep a full grasp of the historical events about to take place in the world. At the same time I stressed that we were merely there to help, that he was a good and easy patient to manage and that we were pursuing no ulterior aims, but from his point of view there was a strong case for further treatment.

"The result of these quite protracted talks (in which he was especially lucid) was that he fell back on his aversion to drugs, on our assurance that his mind would, anyhow, recover some time, which was all he had wanted, and on the merciful veil of 'nescience' which was helping him to bear his captivity more easily. He made it abundantly clear that he did not wish for a second 'ordeal' such as had taken him all his willpower and courage to undergo. During these conversations he was friendly but very fidgety. There was no hint of recognition.

Summary: "The patient's mental state after Evipan treatment was the same as before this procedure. Tests of recognition of familiar names, objects, etc., showed that he had maintained his amnesia. The attitude adopted afterwards proved that this symptom is still highly valued by him, while the notion of 'drugs' also mobilises his persecution and poisoning fears.

Future Action: "Major Ellis Jones promised that he would seize any favourable opportunity for further treatment. If necessary, I could be sent to Maindiff Court at short notice, e.g., by road. It proved needful to have a German-speaking psychiatrist present, as the patient's English only returned towards the end of the session."

APPENDIX

FULL MEDICAL NOTES ON EVIPAN NARCOSIS ADMINISTERED AT MAINDIFF COURT ON MAY 7TH, 44

1900 hrs. Patient had a light meal.
It was noted that he had prepared two glasses of cold water standing in hot water (his way of taking the chill off) prior to treatment.

2045 hrs. Patient in bed. Present: Dr. Phillips, Dr. Ellis Jones, Sgt. Everett and a cpl., R.A.M.C. Ante-cubital fossa, left, sterilised. Vein identified; 5.5 cc. Sodium Evipan solution slowly injected intravenously.

2100 hrs. Dicks enters. Patient ceasing to count, muscles fully relaxed. Snoring. Needle withdrawn. No bleeding. Pad on wound. Coramine prepared. Pulse and B.P. steady.

2110 hrs. Begins to stir. Suggestion by Dicks in German: "You will now be able to recall all the names and faces of your dear ones. Your memory will return. We are all here to help you. Dr. Jones is here. He is healing you," etc., slowly repeated. This sort of suggestion was repeated also later, throughout the session.
(Henceforth verbatim notes: Dicks's and patient's words translated).

2112 hrs. Groans.

D. What troubles you?

Pt. Pains! In my belly! (Severe groans.) Oh if only I were well. Bellyache (groans). Water! Water! Thirst!

D. You will soon have water. Tell us now what you have forgotten.

Pt. Oh, I don't know. Pain! Thirst!

D. You will tell us now what you have forgotten.

Pt. Water! Pain in my body! A fog . . .

D. Remember your little son's name?

Pt. (whispers) I don't know.

D. Your wife's: Ilse it is.

Pt. I don't know.

D. You remember your good friends, Haushofer. . . .

Pt. No.

D. Willi Messerschmitt.

Pt. No. (groans) Bellyache! Oh God!

D. Why this pain?

Pt. . . . (groans).

D. And how you lived in Alexandria as a little boy.

Pt. No.

D. And all the stirring times with Adolf Hitler in Munich.

Pt. No.

D. You were with him in the fortress at Landesberg.

Pt. No.

D. Come, it will help you to tell us all that hurts you.

Pt. Pains . . . (repeated). I don't know . . . (repeated).

D. But Ilse you know.

Pt. I don't know.

Jones. Speak and answer, it will help. (In English.)

Pt. Speak and answer (echolalic repetition). Leibschmerzen (bellyache)!

D. You have had these for years.

Pt. For years. Bellyache!

D. You will recall all the other parts of your past.

Pt. Recall all the other parts.

D. All the great events of your life.

Pt. All the great events. (More groans and calls for water.)

D. Your boy's name?

Pt. The boy—his name? (Groans.) Oh, bellyache. (Terrific groans.)

Jones. Why do you groan?

Pt. (in German) Bellyache, bellyache.

D. Why this self-torment, why give yourself so much pain?

Pt. (Shouts out in groaning agony.)

D. How did the bad pain get inside you?

Pt. Water, water!

Jones. You speak, it will do you good.

Pt. (groans).

D. Why do you torture yourself?

Pt. Water!

D. Who has done you wrong?

Pt. I don't know.

Jones. Come, come, tell us why you are in pain; speak, we want to help.

Pt. Pain, water! (Groans.)

Jones. Now tell us what was your wife's name, and your boy's?

Pt. (in English) Wife's name, and your boy's . . .

Jones. You were in Alex. as a little boy, remember? And how you told me that father took you to school, your trips to Sicily (etc.) your visits to the circus.

Pt. (responds only by echolalia of the last words in each of many English sentences).

Jones. And your Army service in Roumania.

Pt. I don't know (English).

Jones. Haushofer—he was your dear friend. And Sauerbruch, the great surgeon, who operated on your wound? Remember your wound?

Pt. (no reply, but Phillips and Jones note a quick gleam of recollection at these two stimuli).

Jones. But at least, who are you? And your wife?

Pt. (confidently repeats his name). And your wife?

At no point did the patient make a spontaneous remark: the sole unprovoked utterances were groans. This was followed by repeated exhortations that here were all his old doctors eager to help him, but he sat up and said: "Water please, and some food." I quietly withdrew. The session ended at that point, 2215 hrs.

CLINICAL POINTS

"Dr. Phillips and I agreed that the pain was pushed to the forefront, just as it is at awkward waking moments, as a defence. The conscious preparation as shown by the glasses of water was also noted. A case of hypochondriasis seen and repeatedly evipanised by me at Stanboroughs in 1940 behaved in a similar "pre-defended" manner: worse after the first session.

Jones holds the "prison-disease" theory. This is supported by the patient's own valuation of his amnesia as a defence against both boredom and mental distress. His seizing on the reassuring element in Jones's remarks after the session, and his resuscitation of the drug-phobia, made us all feel that the defences were too strong and the incentives too weak for success. During my talk next day, when I argued that he was hurting his wife, losing much interest in life, etc., he said: "It is all the same to me—what is the difference? I don't care whether I talk to anybody." This evidence of pretty profound narcissistic régression makes us feel pessimistic about the outcome of further Evipan sessions that may be undertaken."

After this a few fuller extracts from the consultant's reports may be given.

June 6th, 1944.

"—he is much less worried about his loss of memory and a good deal more cheerful all round. There is at present no evidence of the old delusional ideas. The loss of memory is still as complete as it was. His attitude to it is now very frankly that since he is quite reassured that his memory will come back he thinks it a very good thing to have lost it for the time being. He has fastened to the window opposite his writing table a note he has written keeping him reminded that he should not have any more injections because he feels the last ones made him feel a little muzzy, and reminding him further that his memory will come back."

The actual document is reproduced here.

September 5th, 1944.

"—His general health remains very good; he has still got his abdominal cramps, but these have not varied or become any more serious than they were. They still tend to come on

No more injections!

The first injection has not improved the memory in any way, but instead provoked great nervousness.

The replies to the questions put during the experiment have proved that memory is still in existence and only transitorily disturbed. The doctors are convinced it will come back in Germany. So do not worry and no excitement if memory is still so bad at the moment and you cannot even recognise people whom you have met before.

At all events no 2nd injection!

DOCUMENT REFERRED TO ON P. 90, WITH ITS TRANSLATION

nightly at about 7 p.m., which coincides with the German news bulletin, and there is no further evidence that there is any physical factor operating to cause this discomfort. His memory is still lost, and my conviction that this is a true amnesia was renewed on this visit and confirmed by the experience of the commandant and his officers as well as by the medical men. He is quite clear that to recover his memory would mean facing many unpleasant and unhappy memories of failure, and consequently he still does not wish it to be recovered. I had a long talk with him about the moral aspect of this attitude of mind towards his own failures and unpleasant circumstances, and it should be interesting to see if it has any effect—I rather doubt it.

"Amongst various bits of writing which he has pasted on his window to keep himself reminded of things in view of his loss of memory, is an extract from a letter written by his wife, in which she states that she quite understands the situation, that she has consulted doctors in Germany about his amnesia and they have told her that it is clearly the type which will recover after the war is ended, and that she feels satisfied."

December 19th, 1944.
"With regard to the suggestion that if he went to Switzerland he might recover I am strongly of the opinion that such a visit would not produce any result beneficial to his present condition."

February 15th, 1945.
Report by Lt.-Col. Dicks after the lifting of amnesia (Feb. 4th), the suicidal gesture and the declaration that his amnesia had been simulated.

"I visited Maindiff Court on February 12th and 13th, 1945, in place of Brigadier J. R. Rees, at present overseas.

"I learnt from the physicians in attendance the recent medical history of the case. I found arrangements for the patient's comfort leaving nothing to be desired in view of the need for strict supervision.

"I was able to see, and talk to, the patient for considerable periods. The patient has made a very dramatic recovery from the temporary affection of his memory, which now functions very fully and accurately.

"I cannot accept his own statement that the memory loss never existed. There was at that time a true partial dissociation of the personality, which permitted the patient to 'take in' what was going on around him, but caused difficulty of recall. It is a case of preferring to have duped us to having shown temporary weakness.

"His present physical condition is good. Appetite and intake of food are returning to normal after a recent protest which was overcome by peaceful persuasion from Dr. Phillips and Major Ellis Jones. His superficial wound is healing satisfactorily.

"The recent acute phase of suspicion and associated excitement, during which he has launched a number of reports and appeals, has now been followed by a much calmer phase. He is very rational, discusses his suspicion as a symptom, i.e., he is prepared to consider it as a creation of his own imagination. In evaluating the recent episode, certain national cultural influences must be borne in mind in toning down the impression of his personal mental abnormality.

"The action taken, abnormal, cowardly and anti-social to our ideas, is almost the normal way out of indignity and loss of face in his ethical code. At present honour is satisfied, after an appeal through the Protecting Power to his own government, in whose hands he leaves the decision whether to eat or to starve.

"Thus I find the patient at much the same level of mental and physical health as when I left him three and a half years ago: i.e., intellectually vigorous and alert; somewhat grandiose and overbearing when acting 'officially', simple and rational, indeed sociable in private; rather egocentric, fussy and suspicious. His suspicions follow lines which can almost be called a stereotyped formula in his normal milieu, and the patient retains some critical insight into them, as before.

"I do not consider it necessary to recommend any changes in regimen. All concerned are aware that a certain risk of impulsive action exists, but short of making his life intolerable these must continue to be taken. At the moment tension has been relieved."

March, 1945.

In view of the statement made once again by Hess that he had simulated his loss of memory, it is extremely interesting to see some of the letters he wrote about this time, one month after his memory had returned. On March 9th, 1945, he wrote to his wife:

"DEAR LITTLE MUMMY,

"Something especially cheerful—my memory has returned again! Better than before. I have not the slightest disturbance any more. The doctors here and at home were completely right in their prognosis. I am naturally very glad about it. For one reason because the consciousness of forgetting everything and not being able to remember most important and most obvious things is most depressing; furthermore because it is easier for me to occupy myself and to read difficult books the contents of which I can remember and work upon. In brief it is on the whole a great and happy event for me."

Then follow three foolscap pages full of detailed messages of various kinds. On March 14th, 1945 he wrote to his aunt, Frau Rothacker, in Zurich:

"As in one of your letters you sympathised with my loss of memory I want first of all to report a happy event to you; my memory has returned. It is as good as it was before even if it is not better. The doctors here and at home were therefore right in their prediction. The cessation of the disturbance is a great relief to me because it is easier for me to occupy myself. I can read serious books again and I can occupy myself mentally."

He goes on at great length to her, full of chat of all kinds about events and people.

An earlier letter to his wife written soon after his loss of memory is quoted on page 79. Nearly every letter that he wrote during this period had references to his loss of memory. These epistles written in March áre so different in their tone and quality and length as to provide reassuring proof, if it were needed, of the genuineness of what had happened.

April 20th, 1945.

"—Hess's personality has (apparently) quite changed now that the hysterical amnesia has disappeared and he is back now to somewhat the same condition that he was in in the early days at Mytchett Court, only rather more obviously unbalanced mentally. He has recaptured all the arrogance and rudeness that he then had and is, of course, in consequence a much more difficult patient to manage than he has been for a long time.

"The patient at the moment is, of course, under constant supervision. A mental nursing orderly is with him day and night and this will have to continue. He had no complaints save that the old abdominal discomfort still continued—

"It is quite certain that his delusional state is a good deal more marked than it ever has been while he has been in this country. Probably this is due to the greatly increased external tensions that come from his reading of *The Times* and his listening to the radio. It must be accepted that there is a continued risk of suicide and that no amount of precautions, such as constant attendance, can give a hundred per cent guarantee against that. He has not been out of the building lately and shows no wish to do so, which is just as well."

June 22nd, 1945.

"To sum up for the purpose of this present report, Hess is undoubtedly a constitutionally unstable man—a constitutional psychopath, to use a technical word. He has probably for many years had a paranoid or delusional tendency and has certainly shown that markedly during the time of his captivity in England whilst I have had him under my care. If one saw him to-day for the first time he would give the impression of suffering from a paranoid psychosis. At the same time he has, I think, at all relevant times so far as is possible to judge been responsible for his actions. He certainly is at the present time, and he also is at the moment certainly able to plead in a court of law. As a matter of fact he is looking forward to this very much and has, I understand, prepared an extremely lengthy statement for that purpose. Physically he is well; mentally he is as well as he has been at any time in this country.

"We have here a fairly common picture of a man who intellectually is able and clear-headed even though his points of view and arguments are in part the result of a distorted or abnormal mental outlook, and this co-exists with the fact that he is suffering from psychosis and is potentially suicidal and also probably homicidal. His impulsive tendencies would probably only show themselves again were he to feel himself in some extremity or under conditions of what would appear to him peculiar stress.

Although in peace-time he could and would carry on without any special care, under the present circumstances he will still need constant supervision, and may at any time become more markedly abnormal than he now is.

"I had the opportunity yesterday of discussing the situation afresh with my two colleagues at Maindiff—Dr. Phillips, who is an elderly and very experienced civilian psychiatrist in charge of the Monmouthshire Mental Hospital, and Major Ellis Jones, who is in daily charge of the prisoner. They agree with the point of view I have expressed in this report."

July 19th, 1945.

Major Ellis Jones wrote:

"As I stated in my last letter, the patient is more agitated and suspicious. On 13.7.45 he again reverted to the condition that you have previously seen him in, best described I think as a pseudo-dementia. The loss of memory is again grotesque, e.g., loss of memory for prominent places in Berlin, that he was Deputy Fuehrer, failing to recognise one nurse who has been here for two years, etc."

CHAPTER VIII

HESS'S OWN STATEMENT

The following statement was written by Hess during his time at Maindiff Court, was taken by him to Nuremberg amongst his possessions and there was translated. The translation was, of course, made by an American. This interesting document needs no comment.

I LANDED on the 10th of May, 1941, at 10.45 p.m. in Scotland, I was taken to Glasgow by car, where I was imprisoned in a cell in the police prison. Only after I protested because of my injured leg and when I demanded to see a doctor was I taken to hospital. There they had guards standing beside my bed with fixed bayonets. This was my official reception in England!

Somehow, though, I had been received by the English people. My parachute landed me about 10 feet in front of the door of a small farm-house. The inhabitants took care of me very well. They helped me to get into the house, put a rocking-chair near the fireplace and offered me tea. Later, when I was surrounded by British soldiers, a young Tommy got up and gave me a bottle of milk which he had taken along for his guard duty. He told me to drink it as it would be good for me after my flight.

In all these cases, people did not know who I really was. It was the reception of an unarmed enemy whose name was not known. From that I deduced that the ideals of fairness and fair play had not yet died in the English people.

Next morning, the Duke of Hamilton came to see me after I had requested that. After I told him my name, I explained to him why I had come. At the end, I told him somehow my feeling of what the future held in store for me and I had had that feeling already in Germany. I told him that I had flown to England to render a service to the peoples that had been involved in the war but had not come to go through a Secret Service third degree. I was regarding myself as an emissary and in that capacity I asked for the protection of the King of England, to whose honour and fairness I appealed. The Duke replied that the Secret Service was being misunderstood in Germany. Things as I apparently imagined them are impossible in England. However, he was going to inform the

King and other interested persons of what I had said to him.

The same day, I was moved to a hospital in Drymen near Glasgow. About eight days later I went through London and was moved into a house south of the city. I was not told for half a day where I was. It was being kept secret. Only shortly before the visit of the Swiss Envoy in December was it thought necessary to tell me that I was in Mytchett Place near Aldershot.

The Scottish officers, who up to that time were near me, behaved correctly. They even tried psychologically to make my position easier. The English major who was responsible for moving me behaved like a heel, as also did some officers who were at that time in Mytchett. They were officers of the Guard and I was told that they were there by order of the King in order to guarantee me that I was under his protection. Also, a doctor from Drymen, a Doctor Graham, who until that time had behaved beyond reproach, suddenly got fits of bad manners. In Mytchett I was constantly awakened from sleep, partly by the officers who came into my room with a lot of noise and who flashed a strong light on my face, allegedly to make sure that I was still alive. Partly, also, by the many air-raid alarms and all clears which sometimes went up to four a night and which were repeated by sirens and horns that were mounted on the house.* I could hear neither the noise of motors nor anti-aircraft fire. If I tried to catch up on my sleep during the day, this was prevented by constant slamming of doors; people running up and down stairs on a stairway which was apparently right over my room.

For four weeks I was prevented from reading any newspapers or magazines and the people round me were ordered not to mention anything to me which might give me an idea of what was happening in the world.

Already, when I arrived in Mytchett, I instinctively distrusted the food. Thus, I did not eat or drink anything on the first day. Then it was suggested to me to share my meal with the doctor and the officers. Although instinctively I did not want to eat together with members of an enemy nation, I nevertheless thought it was more important at the moment to keep my body healthy than to give in to feelings. It soon became apparent

* This was not in fact the case. There were sirens at the neighbouring Army School of Hygiene, about 300 yards distant. Ed.

how justified my misgivings had been. They offered me food and drinks constantly which the others would not accept. Once, when I was careless and drank a little bit of milk by myself, a short time later I got dizzy, had a terrific headache and could not see straight any more. Soon thereafter I got into an hilarious mood, and increased nervous energy became apparent. A few hours later, this gave way to the deepest depression and weakness. From then on I had milk and cheese brought into my room every day, but merely to deceive the people that I was eating that stuff.

The people around me put more and more peculiar questions to me, touching upon my past. My correct answers evidently caused disappointment. However, loss of memory, which I simulated, gradually caused satisfaction. Finally, I got to such a state that apparently I could not remember anything any more that was further back than a few weeks. Then a conference with Lord Chancellor Simon, of which I had been informed before, was planned for the 9th of June. I was convinced that the obvious endeavour to weaken my memory had some connection with that conference. I suspected that I was to be prevented in this manner from making any proposals for an understanding and that moreover Lord Simon was to receive the impression that I was mentally not normal because I was not capable of answering the simplest questions that were to be put to me. Thus, in order to be safe, I did not eat anything the last three days before the conference except for drinking some water. When he came I had some wine brought up to my room, but instead of drinking it I poured it away. Major F.*, a German-speaking officer who was with me, was informed by me that the wine had caused a miracle, my memory had suddenly returned completely. I shall never forget his horrified and confused face. However, the conference could not be called off any more since Lord Simon was already in the adjoining room. I was well enough for a conference lasting two and a half hours, even though I was still under the influence of a small amount of brain poison. I gave Lord Simon the reasons for my coming to England; I gave him a few facts about the period leading up to the war and told him some other things of which I thought they might be psychologically unaware in

* Name deleted by Editor.

England and made some suggestions to him in order to end the war. Since witnesses were present during the conference I told the Lord Chancellor afterwards how I had been treated. However, he could not believe my statements and he left convinced I had become a victim of prison psychosis.

After the conference I informed the British Government, first orally and later by written protest, that I was an emissary. I gave the following reasons:

1. I had come to England voluntarily and without arms and there was no ammunition in the guns of the plane.

2. I declared immediately after my arrival to the Duke of Hamilton that I had come to end the war and that I wished to make proposals to the British Government with that end in view.

3. Evidently the British Government did not recognise the declarations of the German Government that I was not acting on their behalf, otherwise they would have refused even to talk to me. On the contrary the British Government, three weeks after the publishing of the German declarations, initiated a conference with witnesses and stenographers present, to which they sent the highest dignitary of the Empire after the King, who emphasised that he was there on behalf of the British Government in order to hear my proposals and to discuss them.

Thus, it had to be taken into account that the treatment which I described had been given to a man who must be recognised as an emissary by the British Government.

A few days after the conference, I broke my leg.* With the excuse that he was giving me morphine, the doctor injected brain poison into my body from a syringe holding about fifty c.c. and I felt the effect shortly afterwards. I was given more morphine a little later, though from a small syringe† and then I was put in a cast. The same day, Brigadier-General Dr. Rees of the British War Office came to see me in order to ask me as to the reason for this behaviour. He was very affable and promised to initiate an investigation. He came back the next day. His behaviour was completely changed. He declared abruptly

* It is curious that neither here, nor later in writing of Abergavenny, is there any mention that this was an attempt at suicide. Ed.

† The same syringe was in fact used on both occasions—but for the first injection distilled water was given for reasons explained in Chapter V. Ed.

that I was a victim of prison psychosis and was suffering from auto-suggestion. As a matter of fact I was being treated extremely well. The strangest thing here was how his eyes had changed since the previous day. They had a peculiar glassy and dreamy expression. It appeared hopeless to change his opinion and to convince him of the correctness of my allegations. Dr. Dix (sic), who was detailed to be with me, gave me what were supposed to be pills against pain and that were supposed to make me sleep. They did not have any such effect. Instead of that my bladder became closed and for twenty-four hours I could not pass any water.* The doctor recommended to me to drink lots of water but the only result was a further increase of my suffering. Then I tried to deceive him by merely making it appear like I was taking the tablets and then my bladder could not close any more. If I took only a small part of the pills the cramps which would close my bladder would start again. Repeated experiment always had the same result.

When I refused to take any more pills they then apparently put the same thing in my food, which I noticed by making further experiments when, in order to alleviate my pain, I drank only a very little water, they put an excessive amount of salt in my food so that thirst would force me to drink. There was a certain Lt. M. with me who was distinguished by his extreme politeness. It can well be understood however that he could not believe that the pills had such a peculiar effect. He said such things are not possible in England. However, in order to experiment with it, he took one of the pills which I had kept for him. When he came back the next morning, I could not bring him to discuss the result of the experiment. There was no more politeness. His eyes showed the same peculiar change as the eyes of Brigadier-General Rees had undergone. A few days later he looked normal again; however, his behaviour remained unaltered. A few days later Lt. M. was promoted to captain after jumping the rank of first lieutenant and he told me that even in the British Army this was a most extraordinary procedure so far away from the front. This same startling promotion was also given to Lt. S., who had tried one of my experiments without success.

* This is not a correct statement. No pills were administered on the day of setting the fracture. Ed.

Of course, the aim of all this was to cause my nerves to collapse. The same goes for the extreme restriction in reading material. It was said that any edition of Goethe could not be obtained in the whole of England. It could not even be borrowed, it was said.* This same goes for a German history of the world. I could not even get a German text-book of higher mathematics or medicine. I only received a few English books from time to time. However, I was given an English novel which told of a little boy of the age of my own boy. Every page was to remind me of my child and I was to be reminded that there was hardly any hope of ever seeing him again and, if I was to see him again, his father would be crazy without knowing it. Then one day one of the doctors asked me whether my family would be cared for in case something should happen to me. "Of course," I replied. However, he said: "Let's hope so." There they made a mistake, because another officer put the same question on the same day and he used the same phrase.

On the 9th of September, 1941, Lord Beaverbrook came to see me and I told him some things in connection with the German-Russian war which had just broken out.

A few days after the conference on the 5th of September, 1941, I sent a protest to the British Government about the treatment that I was receiving after I had already given a protest to the commandant in this matter. I described a number of events that had taken place. No matter whether this had happened with the knowledge of the British Government or not, they nevertheless were responsible for it. I expected that they would investigate this scandal at once and would punish those responsible. By the way, my honour was in no way implicated by this treatment, but only the honour of those who had ordered these things to be done. I received no answer.

I did not choose the official channels for my protest, because then the German Government most certainly would have received knowledge of it, if it had gone by way of the Swiss Envoy. However, I wished to spare the Fuehrer the knowledge of my plight. After coming to England on my own initiative and thus being responsible for my own position, I wished to get out of it on my own.

* In fact, one of us (H. V. D.) lent Hess his volumes of Goethe's works within a few days of his request. Ed.

After the cast* was taken off in Fall, I was moved into a room whose windows were facing the street. Motor-cycle exercises took place on that road every day for several hours, and I was told that it was merely by accident that it was taking place in this locality. I was furthermore told that sixty pupils were taking part in it. Again by accident they chose the road right in front of my quarters for their training ground and a racket developed that was unusual even for motor-cycles, and which could be only explained in such a way that the mufflers† had been doctored. When the motor-cycles were not going, machine-guns would shoot in the intervals during the day. Planes circled the house at extreme low levels. Powerful air-raid sirens screamed in between and I was told that this noise originated in an aerodynamic wind tunnel.‡

Of course, I thought constantly how the monstrous behaviour of the people around me might be explained. I eliminated the possibility that they were criminals because socially they made an extremely good impression. Also, their own past contradicted that assumption.

Brigadier Rees was a nerve specialist of reputation and internationally known as a teacher. He took part in medical conventions on the Continent and in America and even in Germany; he spoke a little German and expressed his sympathy for Germany.

The commandant of the camp, a Lieutenant-Colonel S. of the Scots Guards, was a painter in civilian life. He had a most sensitive personality. His piano playing was extremely beautiful whenever it penetrated into the sick-room.§ He played Mozart and Haydn with most extraordinary feeling.

Major F. allegedly had worked in the British Consulate-General in Berlin in peace time; he spoke German without an accent. He was an older gentleman and very nice. When he was transferred after and said good-bye to me, tears came to his eyes. I observed the same thing also with the other officers.

Lieutenant, or rather, Captain M. of the Scots Guards was the

---

* For British readers—the plaster in which Hess's broken leg was splinted. Ed.

† i.e., silencers.

‡ The area contained a military police motor-cycling school, Farnborough experimental airfield and, of course, many infantry units in training. Ed.

§ Alas for Col. S.'s fame—this was a radiogram. Ed.

son of a regimental commander from New Zealand, who was killed in 1915 at Gallipoli. His ethics were very high. It was his intention to work in the youth movement after the war.

A Captain P. of the Guards was a son of a court chaplain at the Court of George V, then the English King. He has a delicate soul and body. During his tour of duty with me his father died. He told me how deeply he was stirred by the death of his father. However, this did not prevent him a little later, when I received the news of the death of my own father, from participating in the general endeavour to cause my nerves to collapse, with the arrival of this favourable opportunity.

There was a number of officers, among them the sons of some of the best English families. I liked almost all of them. The same goes for the doctors and nurses.

Since none of them were criminals, the thought was natural that they must be lunatics. However, in contradiction of this was that, apart from their behaviour towards me, they had no abnormal traits. They gave me the impression that they were quite normal. The thing that I noticed most were the eyes of Rees and M., which had undergone some temporary change, which, however, might be explained by too much drinking of alcohol. Above all, it was not known to me that there was some medicine which could put a human being arbitrarily into a state of partial lunacy in which they would carry out without scruples whatever is suggested to them or whatever they are ordered to do.

A further thought that I had was that these people had been hypnotised, although at the time I did not know that there was any possibility of causing such a strong and lasting state of hypnotism. I expressed this suspicion quite frankly to Major F., who evidently regarded this as a wonderful joke. He said that he and all others around me were absolutely normal, and unfortunately I was merely the victim of auto-suggestion. He regretted this deeply. Nothing else could be expected but that the fact of finding myself suddenly in captivity would have a corresponding effect on my nerves. All those around me constantly endeavoured to make my life as pleasant as possible. Thus it was all the more painful to them to meet time and time again my suspicions, and to be accused of criminal acts.

In this and a similar manner the people around me played

their parts with the greatest zeal and tenacity. Sometimes it even seemed to me that they believed what they said. One day Lieutenant-Colonel W. called a meeting of the officers of the camp along with Dr. Graham, in order to give me the word of honour of all those present very solemnly that nothing harmful was being put in my food or the medicines that were given to me. The fact that officers were giving a false word of honour supplied the final crowning touch.

In November, 1941, I got in touch with the Swiss Envoy in London, and asked him to visit me as the representative of the Protecting Power. I had hardly mailed the letter when, again, huge quantities of brain poison were put in my food to destroy my memory, after I had not been given any of this poison for a long while, nor any of the poison which closed my bladder. Again I deceived them into believing that I had lost my memory. After I appeared to have lost my memory completely, the Envoy appeared. Although I did not receive any wine, which had wrought a great miracle in the case of Lord Simon, my memory suddenly reappeared. I handed a letter addressed to the King of England and dated the 13th day of November, 1941, to the Envoy. In this I insisted on the protection which had been promised me and described the treatment that I had received, and I appended a copy of the protest which I had sent to the British Government on the 5th of September, 1941. I expressed the suspicion that the people around me had been mentally deranged by a criminal act. Only by that could their behaviour be explained. I recommended having the medicines of the doctors confiscated without previous warning, in order to confirm my allegations. I went on to state that I had not informed the Swiss Envoy of any of this; on the contrary, it was my desire to give the King an opportunity to intervene without informing the German Government of what had happened, through the Swiss Legation. I appealed for the second and last time to the fairness and honour of the King of England. I asked the Envoy to transmit this letter personally and, if this should prove impossible, to give it to the Duke of Hamilton.

After the visit of the Envoy, I was given a daily dose of brain poison for eight weeks. After the second failure they apparently wished to find out whether I was immune. When it was found out unmistakably that I was not losing my memory, they gave it up.

They tried then all the more to effect a nervous collapse in order to give any further statements about my treatment the appearance that they had come from a lunatic and thus were not to be taken seriously. Daily, they caused my bladder to close and only let it open once for a short time in twenty-four hours. Apart from the salt, the hottest Indian pepper—curry—was put in my food to make me thirsty. I suffered indescribably during this period. Finally, however, the medicine did not have the desired effect any more. Once, when the doctor tried to ask me in a very affable manner whether I had had any previous illnesses, I was careful enough to tell him that one of my kidneys was slightly out of order, and therefore I had recently eaten only slightly salted foods or foods without any spice at all. Then they put so much salt in my food that even the nurses, after I had made them taste some of the food, admitted that the food could not be eaten although they themselves were used to eating strongly spiced food. All of my complaints were without success. Major F. declared that a new cook had arrived, and he could not remember that he was supposed to put less salt in my food. After a few weeks they examined my urine; apparently the result was such that they gave up all hope of inflaming my kidneys and after that they only put the normal amount of salt in my food.

For three years, they caused my intestines to close by a medicine that they put in my food and it could only be opened by a special antidote. At the same time, they put the strongest laxatives in my food which caused me terrible stomach and abdominal cramps several times daily. Only at intervals of several days did they make it possible for me to empty my bowels, and after the next meals they would close again.

They refused to give me any pills against pain, but rather they gave me pills which did not have any effect. Heat had some effect against pain—hot water bottles which were given me on the other hand increased the cramps by their weight. They claimed that an electric heating pad could not be obtained in the whole of England. As a matter of fact, electric heating pads were offered for sale at this time by the English Press. As for instance on the front page of *The Times* of

November 8th, 1941—A warm dry bed—Glove Company, Chapel-on-the-Furth (*sic*)—my reference to that ad. was futile.

Twice or three times I was really given a pill against pain. Soon, however, I was told such pills were no longer available in England. A few weeks later, I received fifty Anadin-Anazin tablets for use as I saw fit, whereas so far I had received the smallest quantities of medicine at one time. It is quite clear what effect the taking of several tablets daily would have had on my nerves. Only with the greatest willpower could I restrain myself. In the position in which I found myself the handing over of fifty tablets signified that I was now given an opportunity to end my torture forever, in the most comfortable manner. When however I did not make use of this possibility they increased my pain still further by giving me huge amounts of curry almost every day in order to irritate my bowels further. After I protested, Major F. replied, and Dr. Johnston also agreed, that curry was excellent against troubles of the stomach and the bowels; thus also this protest was fruitless.

Since there was a great lack of books, I spent a large part of the day in drawing architectural sketches—suddenly my eyes got so bad that I could neither draw nor write nor read. At this time I took breakfast as my only meal without company, and thus it was the best opportunity to give me poison. For a few days, I merely pretended to eat breakfast and at once my eyes got better. I had hardly started drinking the cocoa again when the visual disturbances reappeared. When it was noticed that I was not eating breakfast any more and that my eyes had recovered, the poison doubtlessly was put into my other meals. I suspect, though, that it was put in some part of the food which the doctor would be careful not to eat. Soon my eyes deteriorated so badly that I could see only very blurry outlines of near and distant objects. I had to take into account the possibility of becoming blind. My eyes secreted so much liquid that they were completely glued up in the morning; when I told this to the doctor and Major F. their faces took on an expression of demoniac satisfaction. They declared however at the same time that this was terrible and they would have an eye specialist come to see me at once. The eye specialist who had examined my eyes once before all this happened did not show up however. My eyes recovered after a little time so that I could use them again. However, the secretion continued until the end of my captivity. An eye specialist who examined me after more than a year claimed that my eyes were absolutely in order.

As regards my lying in bed with my leg strung up, I had made the request to be given permission to listen to radio broadcasts when I had not received a radio receiver after more than a quarter of a year. Major F. told me that Mr. Churchill had reserved the right of decision regarding my treatment in all its details and so far had not passed any decision about my request. Finally, however, I did receive a radio; when they observed that the listening to the radio gave me a substitute for my eyes which I could not use, they started to make it almost impossible for me to listen to the radio. That the interferences were created intentionally and were made specially for my radio set from very near could be easily found by experiments. They only occurred on the wave-length which I had chosen; if I changed to another frequency abruptly reception would be initially clear. However, a little later the same interference would start again. If I returned to the first station, reception would be perfect until interference followed me there. Then they took the set away to repair it. After that you could not hear any stations except a few German and English stations. I put the radio then on the English Home Service and listened to symphonies and works of German musicians which were presented, whereupon Major F. asked me whether I liked to listen to symphonies—after I said yes, all English stations were blotted out by interference which had German music programmes. Major F. expressed his regrets that, especially during the time when it was important to me to listen to the radio, because I could not use my eyes, the radio should suffer from so much interference.

The last thing that was left to me in order not to fall victim to the deterioration of inactivity was to call back to my memory the contents of books which I had read and things that had happened long ago, and to reflect on problems. Unfortunately, however, they apparently also guessed at this occupation. At any rate, I suddenly got a terrific headache which made any further mental activity impossible. Again I would find by experiment that such an agent had been put into the cocoa; along with the headaches, I had a constant urge to sleep. The doctor expressed the opinion to an officer in my presence that these were the first signs of an inflammation of the brain in its first stages.

I had become very careful in the taking of meals; above all I did not drink any more cocoa. In this way I succeeded in somewhat curbing the amount of poison. Then Major F. appeared and expressed his regrets in a most moving manner that I insisted on making my life unnecessarily difficult. He asked me in my own interest to give up my suspicions and my reserve and to start eating again. He gave me his word of honour that even if something had been put in my food in the past, this would not happen any more in the future. In order to show him that I trusted him and that a new era of mutual confidence had started, I was to begin drinking cocoa again. I agreed. The next time when I received cocoa it contained an inordinate amount of poison.

In the course of the next weeks, I became immune against the poison. At any rate the headache disappeared. My eyes improved so much that I could use them again, but the secretion lasted until the end of my captivity. After a year an eye specialist came, who of course found everything in the best order. Since more than a quarter of a year had passed since I had given my letter to the King of England and to the Swiss Envoy without any result, I again asked him to come and see me. He agreed. When he had not come after three weeks in spite of his promise, I concluded that his visit would be prevented until such time as I would finally exhibit all the signs of lunacy or at least of such great nervousness that people would regard me as not worth believing. A sign for this was the additional poison that was given to me and the increased noise; I pretended to become more nervous from day to day; after I had reached the climax, the Envoy came. I reflected what they had done to keep him away for so long. Then the Envoy told me that he had suffered during the past weeks from an unexplained and bad sickness, accompanied by paralysis; only during the past few days had he become better and so he was coming to see me. One of the after-effects of the paralysis was that he had great difficulty when writing. He repeated what he had already written to me, namely that he had not received permission to transmit my letter to the King personally. The

Duke of Hamilton said that he would have no more to do with my affairs. Presuming that I would agree, he had given the letter to the Private Secretary of the King, Sir Alexander Hardinge, at the end of January, 1942. Now it was April and I had not received an answer. I did not receive an answer later either, not to speak of any change in my treatment. At any rate, not in the direction of improvement. It was the second time that I had appealed without result to the honour and fairness of the King of England. I then told the Envoy everything that had happened at length because I had gotten rid of the nervousness which I pretended to have. The Envoy asked me whether I did not want to move around a little more. I was still walking with crutches at the time. He was convinced that all the things that I had mentioned would disappear; from that I deduced that he too had been told that I was suffering from mental fixations. As proof for the correctness of my allegations, I gave him a few samples of medicine which I had put away. He promised that he would have them examined in a Swiss laboratory.

I wish to emphasise that the Envoy cannot be reproached for believing the statements of the people around me, more credible than my own. How was he to think that a dozen officers, yes, even doctors, all of them making the best of impressions, did not only lie but subjected me to treatment which in part can only be described as torture? In as far as he regarded my complaints as justified, he did everything in his power to effect improvements. He was extremely affable and certainly went further in his desire to alleviate my situation than he had to. He brought me some books from his own library and finally put his entire collection of Goethe at my disposal.

After the visit of the Envoy, everything quietened down. The motor-cycle course was finished, the M.G. gunners had been trained, and the aviators did not have the urge any more to circle around the house where I lived; the plane engineers suddenly did not need their wind tunnel any more and the rooms alongside and over and under mine did not need any more repairs which had involved endless hammering. The soldiers had learned from one day to the next to shut doors without slamming them—in short, paradise-like quiet descended on me. Finally, after a year, I was given the books that had been sent to me from home. They brought me English books from the library. For one year allegedly it had been impossible to get me an overcoat; however, now I received one. The people around me became extremely polite. An astounding change had taken place.

It was quite clear, though, that they would only have me believe that a fundamental and lasting change had been effected in my treatment as a result of the visit of the Envoy—they hoped for a far greater shock effect when they started the noise and the old treatment again, after I had taken breath and given myself to happy illusions.

After two weeks everything happened as expected—new motor-cycle trainees arrived, the same day the machine-gun formations discovered that their training had not been satisfactory yet, and on the same day the pilots again got interested in my house, doors banged, and the doctors and officers competed in rudeness.

In June there was a rumour that I was going to be moved into a very quiet hospital that was somewhere in the country. As a matter of fact I was moved into a hospital at the end of the month, in rural surroundings near Abergavenny in Wales. I was given two rooms in a wing that was apart from the main building.

It became apparent that there was a railroad station a few hundred yards off where they would shunt cars all during the night, in the most noisy manner. The whistles and screeches sounded constantly when the trucks hit each other. There was no thought of sleep; if I tried to catch up on my sleep during the day, this would be prevented by slamming of doors, and hammering just like in my old quarters. One of the nurses smugly assured me that he too couldn't sleep with all this shunting although he was trying to make himself tired by long walks during the day. Dr. Johnston declared that if he had known that there would be so much noise during the night at my new quarters, he never would have suggested my transfer. Even people who are completely healthy would have their nerves damaged here. The doctor in charge of the hospital, Dr. Phillips, told me that he would have to admit that the noise was unbearable. However, people got used to it in good time. He too had gotten used to it—however, it had taken him two years. When I asked him why he put somebody in such a place of whom the doctor said that his nerves were affected, he could not answer.

When the Swiss Envoy visited me again in July, I complained about my quarters where it was impossible for me to sleep. He spent the night in the vicinity; this night was absolutely quiet; whereas otherwise the locomotives would whistle every few minutes, now they were hours between. The Envoy had hardly departed when the racket started all over again.

The Envoy had arrived without giving much previous notice. I had asked him to do this in our common interest; in that way he would not have to suffer from paralysis and I would not suffer from any further increase in the noise. The people around me showed nervousness on the occasion of this visit. The Envoy brought along an affidavit according to which the samples which I had given him did not contain anything harmful. It was made out by a London laboratory. He said, in order to make as little trouble as possible, that he had taken the samples there instead of to a Swiss laboratory. However, he had used a fictitious name so that they would not know their origin. Of course, it was an easy matter for the Secret Service to observe where they were taken and to give orders that nothing should be found in them for reasons important to the conduct of the war. The Envoy, however, was convinced that everything was in the best order and believed more than ever that I suffered from mental fixations.

It became clear to me that all further endeavours to convince him to the contrary would be futile and thus I resigned myself to that. Thus, the only way was eliminated for me which so far appeared hopeful to free myself from this situation. I found myself behind bars for good and behind the bayonets of British soldiers and at the mercy of the most inhuman treatment. A hunger strike would have only meant that poison would have been given to me by forced feeding. Letters in which I only tried to hint at the events around me were lost on the way; as far as possible visitors were not permitted to see me. If the visit could not be prevented, as in the case of the Swiss Envoy, then I was given medicine to upset my memory. In case this didn't work, the visitors were told that unfortunately I was suffering from hallucinations. Apart from that, they must have calculated that what had happened to me was so abominable that already from that my statements would lose all credibility.

I also had the impression that they were collecting material which, if necessary, could be used as proof of good treatment. They put an automobile at my disposal, so that I could go some place where I could go for walks without disturbance from other people. Since I looked at everything from the point of view of whether or not it helped me to overcome my nerves, I used this possibility to move around in the open air in order to bring a little change into my never-changing existence. In addition to the central heating, they put an electric stove in my room. Apparently I did not use it enough to make the electric bill correspondingly impressive so they turned it on behind my back the entire night in my living-room. It was suggested to me to take a hot bath every day, that is a bath in which the hot water changes constantly. Since I did not have any urge to do that, the desired amount of hot water used was arrived at by the nurses forgetting to turn off the tap so that the water was running for hours. The quantities achieved in this matter I suspected would be published at a favourable time to be compared with the general saving by the people of the country, against which I was allowed such extravagance through the desire to make my stay as pleasant as possible. They then filled my entire room with flowers until I declared that in my position I preferred to be without flowers.

The noise from the railroad yards continued night after night —the doctor suggested to me to take a sleeping pill every night. It is well known what harmful effect the continuous use of a sedative will have on the nerves; therefore I declined. Gradually, though, I got used to the noise and slept in spite of it. When they got wise to this, they quit making noises. Thus only the few disturbances remained which are associated with any railroad with much traffic. From that it was clear that the racket which had lasted all the night previously had been made intentionally, partly, apparently, by whistles which had been fastened to bushes in the nearest vicinity of my house.*

They then tried to invent new kinds of noises which I wasn't used to yet. Heavy bangs sounded from time to time, from the

---

* It need hardly be stated that this is a wild flight of the imagination. Ed.

floor of the bedroom; the ceiling of the bedroom, as well as that of the living-room, emitted daily and for many hours a humming noise which caused headaches. After they received the impression that I was used to the monotony they had it increased and decreased or stopped altogether for short intervals. Allegedly these noises were caused by the central heating. They were so careless however that they forgot to let the noises cease at the time of the year when the central heating was not being used.

The guard was posted during the night inside the bars in front of the door leading from the bedroom into the open, where he practised coughing fits, banging his weapons together, and practised loading his rifle. When I complained I was told that as far as possible the guards in the British Army were ordered to stand behind bars during the night, which, of course, was not a very flattering remark for the latter. They played football and cricket against a corrugated iron wall which extended around my so-called garden.

The doctor said, conversationally, that it was very annoying when a radio loud-speaker played continuously. I agreed rather carefully. From the next day on they had a radio, and possibly even a phonograph, start off from 6.30 a.m. until late at night at the greatest volume from a window which was a few feet diagonally across from my living-room; cabaret songs, hymns, and continuous talking, opera music, jazz, sermons, and extracts from operettas followed each other in uninterrupted sequence. When I complained they turned it down, or turned it off altogether for about ten minutes in order to start all over again. This was done for months.*

Such a racket may normally be tolerable. However, in conjunction with chemicals which harm the nerves it will lead to the very limit of nervous collapse, if not actually to madness, which they intended to inflict.

If, in addition to that, the nurses let drop entire trays of noisy objects in the adjoining room and if they quarrelled without end in front of my room, I jumped up sometimes in order to knock one of them down or to choke them. However, I always succeeded in taking hold of myself at the last moment, very often with my hand on the door handle. I knew that then I would

* The guard troops had a radio set in their mess. Ed.

only be doing what the criminals were hoping for in the back of their minds. I imagined myself already in an asylum, clad in a strait-jacket. I knew that in this respect everything would hinge on my endurance until such time as I could call to justice those that were really guilty.

Apart from the doctor in charge, Dr. Phillips, whom I liked very much, there was a Doctor Jones in Abergavenny under whose special care I was put. When he arrived he told me that he would do everything in his power to free me from my stomach and abdominal cramps. He showed that he had interests in many fields. As regards social matters he manifested national socialist and fascist opinions. His criticism of social conditions in England did not lack sarcasm. He had read the English edition of *Mein Kampf*.

On the first day his eyes were clear and he carried himself straight. When he came back to see me on the next morning, a change had taken place. Again the slightly absent-minded glassy eyes. He carried himself limply and bent, and he walked with soft knees. It was especially remarkable that he yawned continuously during the short time that he was with me.

The change in his eyes and the yawning lasted for a few days, then the symptoms left him completely. But he carried himself limply until the end of my captivity.

However, his behaviour to me remained the same until the end of my captivity. It was he who in the major part was responsible for the increased bad treatment and the giving of even stronger poison to me.

Now there could not be any more doubt. This change in the eyes did not come from alcohol. Dr. Jones did not drink, much less would he drink in the morning. The eyes were the symptoms that the people around me had been put into an abnormal mental condition by a secret chemical which had been unknown to the world so far. The condition however is like a partial lunacy, or like a condition which might be created by hypnosis of long duration. In this condition, people can be made to behave like rogues or enemies towards someone for a certain time and to commit crimes such as murder. Then at a prefixed time, under hypnotic influence, they will get excited and will carry out what had been suggested to them. Those suffering from the consequence of such an hypnosis are not conscious enough to act on their own initiative but carry out the wishes of outside influences, as happened with the people around me. Even in them nothing extraordinary could be observed.

With reference to the strange eyes, I remembered the defendants of the trial that took place at Moscow before the war, who accused themselves in the most astounding manner and who, according to reports, had the same strange eyes. Thus the secret chemical had been applied there too, and the victims said that they had been hypnotised into saying what they did say. Just as those around me did what they had been hypnotised into doing. In Abergavenny the periods of closing my bowels were extended to three weeks; since the laxatives which had so far been used became less effective, they now started using stronger ones until finally, even for this particular use, poison was used. Since they were put into all meals, I limited myself to two meals in order to limit the cramps to two a day. Then they started putting several laxatives, which would take effect at different times, into each meal, which again only served a purpose in connection with my closed bowels, because otherwise I would have gotten rid of all of them at one time. Since I hadn't gone crazy in spite of all of this they tried to increase my pains in such a way that they added acids to all my foods which affected my liver and kidneys. Even bread and cake, which had given me relief so far, were finally treated with acid. In desperation, I scratched lime from the walls in the hope that this would neutralise the other stuff but I was not successful.

Gradually, however, my body readjusted; the acids lost their effects. Yes, when because of that they stopped giving me any more acid, it appeared that my previous troubles of a too sour stomach had been completely cured.

However, these people knew how to help themselves. They now started to add corrosive acids to my food. The skin came loose and hung in little bits from my palate. It can be imagined what condition the mucous membranes of my stomach and bowels must have had. Again they gave me food as sour as possible, which burnt the inflamed and injured spots, but in the course of time I became immune also against the corrosive acid.

E

The ill-baked bread which I received regularly and the meat that was so tough that I could hardly chew it, peas that were as hard as stones, beans which the cook again and again forgot to soak before he cooked them, vegetables with mildew and margarine that was more than rancid, evidently were used to cause pain in the stomach and an illness of the bowels. The food tasted interchangeably of soap, dishwater, manure, fish-odour, petrol and carbolic acid. The worst was the secretion from camel and pigs' glands from which even the starchy foods were not safe.

I choked the food down with the greatest willpower as the necessary evil to prevent starvation. The doctor, though, brought me cartoons from the English Press, in which I was feasting at a table that was straining under the weight of delicacies.

As long as a doctor or an officer shared a meal with me during the day, the meal would be slightly better. By the way, though, he would be very moderate when taking food and I suspected that he stilled his hunger later from other dishes. The baker put bits of plum into the cake by mistake.* Meat dishes were crammed with bone splinters, and thousands of small gravel splinters were put into the vegetables. Probably I was to break my teeth on them.

When I needed a dentist urgently at Mytchett, it took four weeks before he came. London was so bureaucratic and was taking so long to approve it when I again got a toothache in Abergavenny my teeth were X-rayed, they put the rays all over my mouth for eight seconds from a distance of three feet for the pictures. When Dr. Phillips told me after the second take that he did not know whether the pictures would come out all right since he did not have any practice, I declined any further X-ray experiments. My suggestion to get the X-rays with a special machine in a dentists' office was not accepted. The dentist who came to see me claimed that he could not find anything wrong, although I could feel it myself and see it in his mirror. They literally let my teeth rot in my mouth.

They gave me alcohol to disinfect a wound, but instead it made it worse; then I made a few incisions with a razor blade. I put the alcohol on one half of the wound and I did not put it

* Plum cake is not unknown in Germany. Ed.

on the other; the first part became infected whereas the latter healed. Thus there was some chemical in the alcohol causing infection; apparently they hoped to be able to cause blood-poisoning.

There was a large concrete area in front of my rooms that were facing the garden and it was covered by a glass roof, and in the summer time unbearable heat prevailed. I could not find any protection in the open from the rays of the sun, since the so-called garden was a lawn about ninety feet square and there were neither trees nor bushes there. I was told that the opaque paint of the glass roof had been removed before my arrival, besides the glass would let ultra-violet rays through. For more than a year I tried in vain to have new paint put on it; even my complaint to the Swiss Envoy remained without success. Finally, they put some paint on the roof which let the light come through. However, the rain soon washed it off again.

They lit fires so that I had to stay for hours in smoke which irritated my eyes.

One hot summer day the air was suddenly filled with the smell of corpses which increased continuously during the next few days. Allegedly it was impossible to find the origin. Finally I went on reconnaissance myself and found that a car load of big fish heads had been thrown into a cesspool which was at a little distance from my quarters and they were decaying in the sun.* When I pointed that out, it was not possible to remove them until the next day, because they claimed that the odour of the cesspool was unhealthy, and thus could not approve it.

When I was no longer able to go for any long walks because of my heart condition I went to a bench which was in the open air for the time that was set aside for that, to read in the shade and away from all the noises; after a few days a bull, whose throat had been cut, was laid down near there, so that the wind would carry the smell of decay and thus made it impossible to use that place.

In order to indulge in some serious activity I started to translate an English book into German. Not long after I had started with that, the tools that I was using for this work,

* Farm land adjoined this wing of Maindiff. Ed.

namely an English-German Dictionary, showed signs of decay that increased from day to day, which increase soon made it useless. Therefore I declared that I had ceased the translation, and continued it only secretly and when I was alone, and gave the appearance of not touching the dictionary any more. Although I used it for another half year as before, there were no further signs of decay.

I did not leave my two rooms in Mytchett. The reason was that they were locked off from the rest of the house by a padlock in front of the bars and there was a military police guard in front of it who kept the key. When I protested, I was told that this was a security measure against attack from the outside, which was further implemented by a number of double guard posts and a barbed wire obstacle. They did not give way to my demand to give me the key for my rooms to keep in order to further increase security; as a consequence to that, I would not leave my rooms as long as they kept me imprisoned there. In accordance with this declaration, I stayed indoors until I was moved to my new quarters, that is about one year. Thus I could only exercise with my crutches, after breaking my leg, inside the room, and I suffered from lack of fresh air. The two windows had been nailed shut whereas the third window could only be half opened because of the bars in front of it.*

The heart poison was without any doubt put into my food and the medicines that were recommended to me to take against my abdominal cramps. My broken leg was also massaged with some powder and this powder was also put into my laundry; it dried the skin and caused unbearable itching of the skin and rashes. They gave me vaseline as an antidote which on the other hand contained heart poison. They put chemicals in my supper that would prevent sleep. The sedatives against this lack of sleep contained heart poison. They did not miss any chances to give it to me.

The result was a condition of utter exhaustion of the heart, but even this apparently was not their final goal. Apparently this was to be achieved by additional strenuous physical activity exhausting the heart.

But my doctors assured me time and time again how much

---

* This was, of course, a precaution against suicide. Ed.

they regretted that I had to suffer so much. I was used to an active life, and the lack of serious activity which was unavoidable during captivity was causing the auto-suggestion that had shown itself in my state, thus all my complaints were merely a nervous condition. They would do for me whatever could be done. They could not even treat their own brother better. One of the officers that stayed with me said that the people around me knew that I was under the protection of the King of England and because of that fact alone it was impossible that those things that I was imagining were really happening. If this was the case, then all the people around me would have to be shot, an opinion to which I could only agree. Also, Doctor Phillips and Doctor Jones gave me their word of honour that no poison was being put into my food or medicines, and I had that confirmed in writing.

In the course of time, I received at least a dozen false words of honour, also from officers of the Royal Guards. When news (of the impending surrender, Ed.) was received, the King of Italy a day before his country went out of the war denied this under his word of honour and thus he too gave a false word of honour. I knew how this staggering event was to be explained, namely that the King of Italy had also been put into a state of partial lunacy.

Dr. Jones assured me that my heart condition was only a consequence of too little exercise. He recommended me to play ball with him and take physical training with him. However, I declined. The noise around me was further increased and it was suggested to me to drive into the country, from the turmoil of my quarters which could not be prevented, and to take the necessary exercise where it was quiet. On the occasion of these trips the car regularly stopped in such a place that I was forced to walk uphill. Yes, they even took me to the mountains. Mountain climbing was, of course, especially good for my heart. Only with trouble could I finally achieve that roads with no grades were chosen. Even on those roads I had to stop continually in spite of walking extremely slowly.

When I couldn't even walk the shortest distance any more without the strongest hammering of my heart or without getting into a condition of exhaustion, Dr. Stott, a specialist in internal medicine with the rank of general, appeared and stated after examining my heart that it was in the best of condition. At the same time, he recommended more exercise, mountain climbing, etc. He, too, had the typically glassy eyes. Apparently it puzzled even the doctors that my heart did not stop after years of poisoning. Dr. Jones asked me twice whether I had ever studied the Apophi doctoring by which immunity against injury and poisoning can be achieved. I truthfully gave a negative answer. This is an example of how they tried to handle everything in order to have a harmless explanation ready.

On the 4th of February, 1942, nurse Sergeant Everett brought me dessert. Unfortunately, the glass dish had been broken and another one had not been available. I asked whether there was any possibility that there were glass splinters in the dessert. Everett replied that this was impossible because the dish had been damaged before filling it. On the strength of my previous experiences, I nevertheless investigated the contents. Everett became very nervous and tried to prevent me from it. There were glass splinters in the dessert. Afterwards, I received the apologies of the cook and it was added that the crack in the dish had been called to my attention before. The mistake had merely been that the filling of the dish took place after it had been damaged. This glass dish, as all other dishes in which I was given poisoned food, bore the monogram of the King of England.* Thus it appears that they wanted to express that I was a guest of the King. The more desperate my situation became, the more the people around me tried to remind me of home. They asked me again and again how my family was although they knew that I had not received any mail for many months. Dr. Jones brought series of pictures of his stepson from the time when he was the same age as my little boy. They played songs from home where I could hear them. A man had been detailed to the guard who had learned to yodel someplace and this was to remind me of my mountains. In the middle of August, 1943, I was informed that a further visit of the Swiss Envoy was expected. At the same time, the worst headaches started which extended all the way into the right eyeball. My sense of time was disturbed. Events that had

---

* This is the cipher G.R. (Georgius Rex) with which all British War Department property is marked. Ed.

taken place days ago appeared to be many weeks away. My memory temporarily deteriorated. I again deceived them into believing that I had lost my memory. I persisted with this even with the Envoy but did not make any impression. His memory too was bad at times. Since his last visit I had lost about forty lbs. and just before he came I suffered from a particularly bad attack of cramps. I looked like a walking corpse. But the Envoy found that I had never looked so well. I asked him to see if I could not be put into a camp for ordinary prisoners of war, since Dr. Jones said that my solitude was responsible for my loss of memory. He replied several times in an amazingly curt manner that he would do whatever was best for me, from which I knew that he would not work for my transfer. I asked him for some books which allegedly they could not get for me any more, Schopenhauer, Schiller, and Gottfried Keller. I reminded him again of the World History which I had requested a year and a half ago. Later he lent me an album of a German humorist. I never saw or heard anything of the requested books, although the Envoy was thereafter in Switzerland, where he was to obtain them for·me.

I have no doubt that the then Swiss Envoy in London was put into this abnormal condition. In this case not so that he would commit crimes but to prevent him from fulfilling my request for books, or from working for my transfer to an ordinary prisoner of war camp, and to cause him to have the samples that I gave him examined in a London laboratory instead of in a Swiss laboratory. Since they were sure that the human tools would be absolutely silent about the execution of these crimes, they could permit themselves the heinousness of bringing about a paralytic condition in the Envoy in order to postpone his visit with me. The new Envoy told me that his predecessor had suddenly suffered from serious disturbance of memory. Finally, for health reasons, he had to return to Switzerland.

I suspect that the crimes against the Envoy were perpetrated in his London Club by people who had been made partial lunatics. I suspect this because the Envoy told me that an old Equerry of the King's belonged to the same club, who had suddenly lost his memory and was found a short time later on the rails after a train had passed over him, without having regained his memory. It is beyond my knowledge what secrets he knew that he had to lose his memory and then be silenced forever. I learned about this case before the second visit of the Envoy through a newspaper article which was published by the *Sunday Times* of March 22nd, 1942, under the heading "The Mystery of the Equerry's Death".

In reply to the request to transfer me which I had made through the Swiss Envoy, the British Government replied that they refused to do so. It would have to be left entirely to them, where and under what conditions they would keep me. I had not expected anything else, and had submitted the request only by way of experiment. A proposal that had already been made before and had been repeated on several occasions to give me a German prisoner of war for company I refused. I could not have taken the responsibility of putting another German at the mercy of this treatment.

My headache went on constantly. I persisted in pretending that I had lost my memory. I learned from my mistakes. I assumed that I must not recognise people that I had seen more than fourteen days ago, even if it was one of the doctors who had been with me for years. From that, it can be recognised what terrible poisons they gave me, a poison for which there was no antidote in existence, in contrast to that I had received in Mytchett.

Soon I didn't make any more mistakes. I came through tests like a sudden appearance of persons whom I had known before, and I pretended not to recognise them any more, although I was in a state of hypnotic sleep. I had to be ready, day and night. Finally, I was ready to answer questions falsely even in my dreams by keeping up the pretence of loss of memory. My hope that in consequence of being ill I would go home proved deceptive. Month after month passed, exchange ships came and went, nothing happened.

In the worry that finally they would succeed in damaging my memory, I learned my experiences and the deductions that stemmed therefrom by heart. I recited them to myself once daily, partly in outline, partly in whole sentences which took several hours. In that manner they would remain in my recollection even if my memory reached back for only a few days.

Dr. Phillips came one day and told me that Field-Marshal

Paulus had appealed to the Germans from a Moscow Radio Station to cease the fight—wasn't it my opinion too that it was time to end the war and didn't I want to go home? I told him, yes, of course, but not at the price of the defeat of my country. An answer which disappointed him visibly. I am convinced that they hoped to be able to obtain a statement which could be used against the German people by propaganda. Even the blackmailing increased. Neither the noise nor a further worsening of my abdominal cramps during the next few days could move me to answer the question which was again put to me in a soothing manner. This event, however, is to me the final proof that the secret chemical had had no effect on me, at least at this time, because otherwise they could force me to be a traitor to my country as Paulus, who, no doubt, became a victim of the secret chemical.

The dentist came on November 2nd, 1944, to examine my teeth. He could not deny any more that they were infected and suggested to me waiting for a few months with the treatment. Since I could not trust a doctor to have any goodwill, I did not insist. The latter insisted however that the crown of the tooth needed a small filling, which I myself did not think correct. However, suspicious though I was of his readiness in this case, I could not object because in keeping up the loss of memory I could not show any suspicion. After the filling the worst nervous pain that could be imagined started in this tooth. The same thing, but not quite so badly, in the other bad teeth. Since it started regularly after the taking of meals and did not occur when I did not eat, it was proved that it was caused by chemical that was put in my food. Gradually, a strong irritation of the nerves developed so that the pain was almost constant. The torture was beyond all limits.

The doctor claimed that this was due to neuralgia. They did not give me any pills against the pain, or rather they gave me pills under this pretence which increased the pain.

The effect of heat against pain was made impossible also in this case by giving me clay or glass bottles, which were useless for treatment of the face. By drinking water extensively, I managed to moderate somewhat the effects of the poisons. When they noticed this, they started to poison the running water, which was the last thing that had remained free of poison

E*

until that time. Experiments which I made by not eating did not leave the slightest doubt.

On the 26th of November, 1944, I asked the Swiss Envoy to request leave of absence for me in Switzerland to restore my health, and I wished to be put under the treatment of specialists there. According to a report by Dr. Jones, either new environment or a shock like seeing my family again would restore my memory to me. I would undertake on my word of honour to return to England any time it was desired. The Envoy, who was the successor of the previous one, came to see me on the 20th of December and told me that my leave of absence unfortunately was impossible because of some fundamental considerations. I asked him to make an alternative request to have me transferred into a General Prisoner of War Camp. When I repeated this alternative request in writing, I received no answer.

After the one-and-a-half-year long pretence of having lost my memory had not effected the desired repatriation, I had to tell myself that the further continuation of this would be futile. Thus, I decided to talk quite frankly to Dr. Jones, if only to see how the doctor would react. He could not hide his surprise that I had suddenly regained my memory to its full extent. I pointed out the numerous happenings in the world, as for example the broken pledge of honour of the Italian King, which doubtlessly were caused by the application of the secret chemical. I pointed out the behaviour of the people around me towards me which could be traced back to the same thing and where false words of honour had played a part. I knew that he particularly, as a doctor, would not tolerate the horrible things that were done to me unless he had been put into an abnormal mental condition. I told him these things, not because I expected that he would admit them; he couldn't do that. However, I wanted to bring him to think about these things and to convince him that he was acting in accordance with a crime that had been perpetrated on him by the use of hypnosis and such means. I had the hope that he would alter his behaviour. As always, his eyes did not meet mine when I started to discuss the subject of happenings around me and when he gave me lies for an answer. They again took on a slightly rigid expression. He said he had to admit that the events in the world which I had mentioned were rather strange, and that they forced him to think; but as far as the sphere of which he could judge was concerned, namely, my treatment, he assured me I was the victim of auto-suggestion. I described to him the various experiments which had provided me with proofs, as for instance, the alternative drinking and not drinking of cocoa. Everything was in vain; I ran into a wall. My treatment was not changed in the slightest. The hope that merely describing the fact would suffice to break the ban proved deceptive.

On the 19th of April, 1945, Brigadier-General Dr. Rees came to see me. He again tried to convince me that my conclusions as well as my suffering only stemmed from mental fixations. I interrupted him with the remark that there was no purpose in his speaking because I knew what I knew. Meanwhile, I had gained further convictions which were adequate to substantiate my suspicions. The abominable atrocities which the British perpetrated during the Boer War in concentration camps on women and children could also be ascribed to the secret chemical. At any rate, I thought that it was out of the question that the officers had poisoned and put glass into my food, that the doctors would have treated me with poisoned medicine, if they had been in a normal condition.

Brigadier-General Rees reflected with a gloomy face. Then he jumped up and hurried out with the words: "Oh well, I wish you good luck."

I had been imprisoned for four years now with lunatics, and had been at the mercy of their torture without being able to inform anybody of this, and without being able to convince the Swiss Envoy that this was so, not to mention my being unable to enlighten the lunatics about their condition. It was worse than being in the hands of criminals, for, with them, there is some little reason in some obscure corner of their brain—some feeling in some obscure corner of their hearts, and little bit of conscience in them. With my lunatics, this was one hundred per cent out of the question. But the worst were the doctors, who employed their scientific knowledge for the most refined tortures. As a matter of fact I was without a doctor these four years because those who so called themselves in my entourage had the task of creating suffering for me and if anything to make it worse. Just as I was without medicine during all this time, because what was given to me under this name only served the same purpose and beside that was poison. In front of my garden, lunatics walked up and down with loaded rifles—lunatics surrounded me in the house—when I went for a walk, lunatics walked in front and behind me—all in the uniforms of the British Army—we met columns of the inmates of a nearby lunatic asylum who were led to work. My companions expressed pity for them and did not sense that they belonged in the same column; that the doctor in charge of the hospital, and who was at the same time in charge of the lunatic asylum, should have been his own patient for a long time. They did not sense that they themselves needed pity. I pitied them honestly—here, decent people were made into criminals.

However, what worry was this to the Jews?—they were as little worried about that as about the British King and the British people. For the Jews were behind all this—if probability alone had not argued for that then the following would have. I was given the book of a Jew, about treatment that he had suffered in Germany in a very significant manner—I was given reports of the British Consulates about the treatment of Jews in Germany according to the description by Jews. Dr. Dix told me that my mental fixations were a consequence of bad conscience about the treatment of Jews, for which I was responsible—I replied that it had not been one of my duties to decide the treatment of Jews. However, if this had been the case, I would have done everything to protect my people from these criminals and I wouldn't have had a bad conscience about it. Lt. A.-C. of the Scots Guards, who was with me for my protection in the name of the King, told me one day: "You are being treated like the Gestapo treats their political enemies." Dr. Dix and the nurse, Sgt. Everett, were present and smilingly agreed.* Since they had stepped out of their regular role, because it was always claimed that I was imagining my suffering, the doctor and the officer were relieved shortly thereafter.

I mentioned the expression used by A.-C. of the Scots Guards in my protest of September 5th, 1941, and added that it

---

* It is thought that this passage refers to the occasion of our attempting to pass a catheter when nerves were frayed by the events of a long and anxious day, when one of the officers present may have said: "We are not the Gestapo." Cf. Chap. V. Ed.

was typical for the Jews to claim that their enemies did what they did themselves. The Hungarian Bishop, Prohaska, had found this already after the Bolshevik domination of Hungary in 1919. He reported that during this period whole truck-loads of mutilated bodies were driven on to the bridges over the Danube in Budapest to be pushed over into the river; that priests had had their caps nailed on their heads, that their fingernails had been pulled out, and that their eyes had been gouged out, and the current joke was why should they go into the other world with their eyes open. All those responsible, with Bela Kun at the head, had been Jews. The world Press had been silenced. However, when, after the collapse of the Bolshevist Government, some of the guilty were to be judged, the same world Press cried out about white terror in Hungary. It has always been like this, Prohaska concluded, whenever a people had to fight against the Jews.

I could not foresee at this time that the Jews, in order to receive material for a propaganda against Germany, would go so far as to bring the guards of German Concentration Camps by use of the secret chemical to treat the inmates like the OGPU did. If I asked myself what the reasons were for the crimes perpetrated on me, I suspect the following—first, the British Government had been hypnotised into endeavouring to change me into a lunatic so that I could be paraded as such if necessary, if they were to be reproached that they had not accepted my attempt at an understanding whereby England could have been spared many sacrifices. Secondly, the general inclination of Jews or of non-Jews whom they had gotten into their power to maltreat me and to revenge on me the fact that National Socialist Germany had defended itself from the Jews. Thirdly, revenge on me because I had tried to end the war too early which the Jews had started with so much trouble, whereby they would have been prevented from reaching their war aims. Fourthly, it was to be prevented that I was to publish the disclosures contained in this report.

The toothache lasted for months. I could hardly carry on any more and I could hardly sleep any more. It was a terrible torture. The doctor advised me constantly against having my teeth pulled; when I finally insisted, the dentist appeared. He did not want to take out the tooth, but wanted to put a filling in it; only when I declared that my teeth were hurting me unbearably but that I would limit myself to the pulling of one tooth, the tooth was pulled. It was the one that bothered me most, although they did not know that. Now that the pain became tolerable I succeeded in bringing my weight back to its earlier normal level.

Apart from the chemical that caused toothache, there was unmistakably a strong laxative and a poison that irritated the mucous membrane in the strongest possible manner. The last was responsible for my nose stopping itself up with congealed blood, that I had a hæmorrhage in my mouth, and that my bowels burned like fire. The doctor could not hide his satisfaction when there were signs of a hæmorrhage in my intestines.

They had been hypnotised to torture me until I became crazy and finally to kill me; to do everything in such a manner that nothing could possibly be proven and that my complaints could be explained by auto-suggestion, at the same time, expressing their regrets about my suffering. Any pity was completely eliminated; while trying to achieve this aim my torture even gave them satisfaction. Any feeling of decency was eliminated, as the following example: I allowed one of the nurses, when he requested it, to take a chair for his night duty which was more comfortable than the one he had. When the chair was brought back, it transpired that the upholstery, which so far had been clean, had been smeared with grease. Dr. Jones lost his fountain pen, which was all the more annoying because it could not be replaced during the war. By accident, I found it on the footpath. The doctor accepted it joyously. To express his gratitude, he brought me a new medicine against my abdominal cramps—it contained the heart poison. Dr. Phillips was very depressed one day, because his son was a Japanese prisoner of war and the British Press published news about maltreatment of PWs by the Japanese. I told them that these statements probably stemmed from propaganda inventions, which I substantiated by pointing out that German prisoners of war had not been treated so well in any country as in Japan. This calmed him recognisably and he thanked me. He, too, used the opportunity to send me a new medicine, which he recommended me to take. It, too, contained the heart poison. Friendly services were thus an occasion for meanness.

Strong pains occurred in my legs. Since the doctor could not hide his satisfaction about this, I could conclude that these were caused artificially.

All my Christmas parcels from home were lost. Dr. Jones brought me a dozen apples on the occasion of the holidays while I was in Abergavenny after they kept them from me for months. He wished me a merry Xmas and that I might soon see my family again. Each apple had been beautifully packed in coloured paper and had been put into an equally Xmas-like box. All apples showed places were they had been penetrated when I sampled them; it was found that hot poison had been injected into them.

Evidently they saw another means of affecting my nerves, by having information appear in the English Press in which I was accused of mean treatment of prisoners. It was just as untrue as everything else published in the Press that came into my hands about other National Socialist leaders.

Note.—Watches—A year and a half and one year—Books— Graham—Scott—Pity with my entourage J—Arrested—interview—perhaps not genuine? Forgotten result of injection—the suppression of the newspapers in regard to the starvation of German—Torture of animals—parcel with cigars—Buren.*

* These notes obviously refer to more bits of "evidence" Hess had intended to write down in detail. The word "Buren" is German for "Boers". It was a favourite "you started it" argument of Nazi propaganda to point to British internment camps for Boers during the South African war. Ed.

CHAPTER IX

THE following notes are written by Major Kelley and give a valuable account of his impression formed in the earliest days after Hess's return to Germany. Major Kelley had of course no knowledge of the detailed history of Hess while in Britain, save what he was given by Major Ellis Jones, who brought the patient over. The conscious elements in this second (or perhaps it should be called the fourth) amnesia were more to the fore.

Major Kelley writes:

"Rudolf Hess arrived at the Nuremberg gaol late in the evening of October 10th, 1945. On his arrival he was met by the commandant, who explained the prison regulations to him. These regulations include the removal of all personal possessions. At this point, Hess became somewhat excited, stated that he was a prisoner of war and a ranking Nazi officer, and demanded that all his personal possessions be placed with him in his cell. The commandant, Col. B. C. Andrus, patiently re-explained the rules and Hess finally relinquished his effects with the exception of a number of packages of what appeared to be documents and small parcels. Hess insisted that these parcels contained material for his defence, including drugs and food which he had brought from England for chemical analysis by an impartial chemist. He offered to permit a guard to remain in his cell twenty-four hours a day, providing these items could be left with him.

"It was pointed out to Hess at this time that his rights and privileges were no different from those of any other German prisoner and that his precious parcels would be sealed and locked in the presence of witnesses. Hess finally accepted this ultimatum and was escorted to the cell where he has remained during the trial.

"His luggage, including his various bundles, were locked up and were not opened until later during interrogation, and while in his presence.

"Physical examination on arrival showed Hess to be in good

physical health, except for some obvious weight loss. A physical examination has been done every month on this prisoner and he was found to be essentially normal. A copy of a typical examination is included as an appendix.

"Psychiatrically, Hess was alert and responsive. His approach and general attitude was reserved and formal, but he gave the impression of making an attempt at real co-operation. His stream of thought was curtailed by his alleged memory deficit, and the majority of his responses consisted simply of 'I do not know. I cannot remember'. This was particularly true when he was being admitted to the prison and his basic history was taken. He stated that he was unable to remember his birth date, birthplace, date of leaving Germany, or any fact or detail whatsoever of his early life. When examined the next morning, he maintained he could not remember anything that had taken place during his imprisonment in England, and only vaguely remembered the plane trip across the Channel. He could remember very little of the details of his admission to the prison, but did recall his parcels and again asked for reassurance that they were in a safe place where they could not be tampered with.

"Hess's mood was somewhat depressed but showed generally normal reactions. In all other spheres except for memory he seemed quite competent and showed no abnormal projections of any type. He was studied daily, and on the 16th of October, 1945, a summary of his psychiatric status was forwarded to Justice Jackson.

"Special examinations done during this period included the Rorschach Ink Blot Test, which was significant in that, while it revealed marked neurotic reactions, it did not indicate any evidence of an active psychotic process. The findings from this test indicate that Hess suffers from a true psycho-neurosis, primarily of the hysterical type which is grafted upon a basic paranoid personality. In other words, fundamentally, Rudolf Hess is an introverted, shy, withdrawn personality, who basically is suspicious of his environment and projects upon his surroundings concepts developing within himself. This paranoid projection is emphasised in his suspiciousness, his desire to have everything 'just so', and is shown in the Rorschach Test by certain types of bizarre responses. These responses however are not sufficiently deviate to indicate a really active paranoid process at present, but indicate the possibility of a psychotic episode. At the time of the examination, however, there was no evidence of actual insanity. His neurotic manifestations on the other hand are quite clearly shown in the Rorschach result and there is no doubt but that Rudolf Hess had a severe psycho-neurosis of the hysterical type. This is demonstrated by marked shock reactions to the colour and shade cards, tension during the test, the crude use of colour and shade and some shifting in the form quality.

"In the psychiatric report of October 16th, it was felt that Hess was suffering to some degree from an hysterical amnesic reaction, but it was equally obvious that a large portion of his total amnesia was deliberately assumed. In view of his hysterical manifestations, which were primarily manifested by stomach cramps, and his hysterical responses to the Rorschach Test, it seemed reasonable to assume that some portion of his amnesia was genuine, but the degree of this reaction could not be determined without special studies. Hess simply prohibited any actual examination of his mental process by blocking every attempt to penetrate it with the response: 'I cannot remember.' No real evaluation could therefore be made at any time and one could only assume that some hysterical mechanisms were probably functioning. This was further evidenced by his complete indifference to his situation and to his amnesia, the so-called 'belle indifference', common in hysteria. The conscious element was patently obvious in the fact that his amnesia shifted in depth from day to day in a most suspicious fashion. On one day Hess would be able to recall events which had occurred three days previously, but on the next interview he would not know the physician or even know what had taken place that morning. He stated that he was unable to read the indictment because by the time he had finished it he had completely forgotten what he had read in the beginning—and yet, at the same time, he was quite able to read thick books which required three or four days' reading time. The spottiness of his reaction indicated obvious malingering and his complete failure to retain anything at all at any time confirms this belief. It was suggested therefore that he be given intravenous sodium amytal or pentothal in an attempt to differentiate the qualities of his amnesia and to determine how much was real and how much was deliberate blocking.

"The suggestion was refused by the American authorities at this time because such techniques, while ordinarily innocuous, in extremely rare instances have untoward results. In view of the fact that the International Tribunal had not yet met, it was felt that this matter should be suspended for their final decision.

"In addition to his amnesia, Hess also demonstrated stomach cramps, which he had had throughout his stay in England and which he has had for many years. These were obvious hysterical reactions, occurring at intervals, particularly when Hess was under observation. He would sit up in bed or on a chair, wrap his arms around his abdomen and rock back and forth, grimacing violently during this time. In spite of the apparent extreme pain, he could break off in the middle of such a demonstration in order to discuss how horrible the pain actually was. At the end of a few moments he would then continue his moaning and grimacing. It was found that neglect was the best remedy for this illness, in fact the only remedy, because Hess absolutely refused to take any type of medication.

"In spite of his total amnesia, Hess seemed to remember a marked distrust of physicians and a violent antipathy toward medicine. Consequently, it was impossible to get him to take anything, even vitamin pills, and it was almost impossible to do physical examinations or blood tests upon him. It nearly required a special act of the Tribunal before he would permit us to withdraw blood for a Wasserman Test, which was negative, and to make a blood group typing, which revealed that Hess is a type 'A'.

"On the 30th of October, Hess's numerous packages were opened in his presence along with a number of other documents which he had brought from England. The packages contained many other little packages, all carefully sealed with numerous red wax seals. In addition, certain parcels of primary importance bore seals on which were affixed his own special imprint 'R.H.'. For the most part, the parcels contained bits of food, chocolate, bread, condiments, sugar, etc., which he had saved from his meals and which, he claimed, contained various types of poison which affected his brain, stopped up his nose, loosened his bowels, plugged up his bowels, weakened his heart, or caused him to lose his memory. He had carefully written on each parcel the result of the alleged poison present. When shown this bizarre collection, he smiled in his usual superficial fashion and denied any knowledge of them whatsoever. He readily admitted that the writing on each package was in his handwriting and identified various documents which were in the lot. He made no attempt to read these documents but seemed content merely to glance at them, identify his hand-writing and hand them back. His only explanation for the time-consuming wrapping and sealing job which he had performed was: 'It certainly seems a good way to pass the time.' At this particular examination it was impossible to determine whether or not he really recognised any of the packages.

"On the 8th of November, 1945, at the suggestion of one of the members of the Court, Hess was shown a series of motion pictures which were collected from newsreels of himself and other Nazis during the days of their greatest power. It was an interesting demonstration but Hess obviously realised what was going on and steeled himself against any evidence of re-cognition. He did however recognise certain scenes, for his hands tensed perceptibly at these sequences. The picture also made an impression on him and he admitted recalling it for several days later. At this time, he stated that in the motion pictures he would never have recognised himself since it had been so long since he looked in a mirror.

"Another test of recognition was administered, and Hess was confronted with Goering, Haushofer and Bohle, all of whom were Hess's oldest friends. He greeted these individuals with a totally blank stare and each one of them was convinced that Hess had totally lost his mind.

"On the 16th of November, Hess was also confronted at an interrogation with two of his former secretaries, Ingeborg Sperr and Hildegard Fath. This was a rather dramatic inter-view. Hess was seated with his back to the door and Fraülein Hildegard Fath was brought in. Hess appeared to recognise her, but demonstrated little emotion and later denied ever knowing her. She expressed considerable emotional response and discussed his family, showing him several pictures of his son. He apparently was little interested and he told her that he had lost his memory. The second secretary was next brought in and Hess evidenced even less reaction on seeing her. At one time, however, during the interview an incident of significance occurred which was noticed by both Col. Schroeder and myself. Hess was asked about a matter to which he replied: 'I do not remember.' Whereupon, his secretary took up one of the pictures and said: 'Here, maybe this will help you to remember.' Hess immediately waved his left hand at her hurriedly and said in a very low voice: 'I do not want any help.' He later denied this, but it was obvious to all present that he did not want to run any risk of giving himself away.

"Hess's relations with his colleagues in the prison were not revealing because he had no opportunity to talk to them before his appearance in the court-room. During his exercise period and during the walks to and from the interrogation room, Hess was handcuffed to a guard because of the history of his suicidal attempts in England. When the trials began, Hess arrived in the court-room carrying a small book, which to the consternation of his co-conspirators he proceeded to read, paying no attention to the trial proceedings. This behaviour upset Goering in particular, who, during the intermission, emphasised to Hess that he still represented the German Government and that such behaviour was beneath his dignity. The general opinion of his colleagues was that he was undoubtedly crazy and most of them pointed out instances in his earlier behaviour which indicated abnormal patterns. Goering emphasised that Hess had always been a mystic, interested in horoscopes and peculiar healing cults. Bohle believed that Hess was quite sane prior to his flight to England but had always been considered by his closest friends as extremely shy, suspicious of everyone and very difficult to talk to about personal matters. He also emphasised Hess's chronic stomach complaints and described Hess's long but futile search for a cure. Hess finally resorted to 'Natural methods', including enemas, rest, heat treatments, etc.''

There should be recorded here one of the reports of the physical examination made on Hess:

SUBJECT: MEDICAL EXAMINATION OF RUDOLF HESS

TO: MAJOR KELLEY

This internee was examined by me on November 10th, 1945, and the findings were as follows:

General: The patient appears to have had an appreciable weight loss as evidenced by the sunken eyes, drawn face, and the prominence of the bony structures of the chest.

Head: Scalp—essentially normal.

Eyes—the pupils are round, regular, equal and react to light and convergence.

Mouth—the mouth and pharynx are essentially normal.

Nose—no obstruction noted.

Neck: There is no evidence of nuchal rigidity. The trachea is in the mid-line. The thyroid is of normal consistency and shows no enlargement. Minimal cervical lymphadenopathy is present.

Chest: The configuration and excursion of the chest wall are within normal limits.

Two well healed linear scars 1/8″ apart are present over the sixth left rib two inches from the lateral margin of the sternum. The superior one is 3/4″ in length and the inferior one is 1/″ in length. A papilloma 1/4″ in diameter is present over the right costal margin slightly anterior to the right axillary line.

Lungs—clear to percussion and auscultation.

Heart—the point of maximum impulse is in the 5th left interspace, 1/2″ medial to the left nipple line. The rhythm is regular and the rate is within the normal variation. A systolic murmur is noted over the apex but is not conducted either into the axilla or up to the sternum; probably functional in origin. The B.P. 110/65.

Abdomen: No evidence of spasticity, tenderness, or masses could be elicited on palpation. The liver and spleen were not palpated.

G.U.: The genitals were externally normal. No discharge was present.

The external abdominal rings admitted the tip of one finger, and a slight impulse was noted on coughing at both sites.

Extremities: Essentially normal. The dorsum of the left index finger shows the faint markings of a scar approx. one half inch in length. There is a patch of chronic dermatitis approx. one square inch in extent on the calf of the left leg.

(Signed) Ben Hurewitz, Capt., M.C.

Capt. Ben Hurewitz, M.C.

Prison Surgeon.

To complete this chapter it is relevant to quote the comments written by Ingeborg Sperr, one of Hess's secretaries. This comment takes very much the same line of hero-worship taken by the other secretary whose report was partially quoted earlier on in the book:

"Since I had little personal contact with the former personal representative of the Fuehrer at that time, I would like to restrict myself to picturing him only as I saw him personally during the course of business.

"When I was twenty-two years old, I came to his Berlin bureau to assist Fraulein Ilse Hillmann, who was his secretary at that time. He had known her personally for many years, and she was also friendly with Frau Hess. The relationship between Herr Hess and Fraulein Hillmann was a particularly good one, and after her marriage it was particularly difficult for me to adjust myself to the position. That I was unable to establish good contact with my chief was due, on the one hand, to my youth, and, on the other hand, to the somewhat introverted nature of Herr Hess. I soon noticed that other people had the same experience as I did. At the same time he was always very kind to all his co-workers and employees, and one felt that it was not just a question of his manner.

Herr Hess was a hard worker, particularly in the first few years of our association. He demanded a lot from his employees and co-workers, as well as the utmost from himself. When he had particularly important things to work on, such as his speeches, etc., he often dictated until late at night.

"When one worked in his vicinity, one must learn to respect this man, whose goal in life was to demonstrate to the German people how to live according to our point of view (Weltanschauung). What impressed me most was his marked 'inner cleanliness' and his willingness to help out other people. On the other hand, he was never able to assert himself against brutal men. It was due to the steady battle that he, in his position, had to wage against those things that were strange and repulsive to his noble nature that this extremely sensitive man's health was finally impaired. He first suffered from insomnia and later from colic pains in the region of the gall bladder. Since the doctors were unable to determine the nature of his ailments, and since their treatments brought no results, he lost confidence in them, went to all kinds of medical quacks, and finally tried with an extraordinary amount of energy to overcome his physical weaknesses. At one time I substituted for Fraulein Fath at his home in Munich, and there experienced him trying out a new method of regaining his normal sleep. At that time he went to sleep at 5.0 o'clock in the afternoon and got up at 3.0 or 4.0 o'clock to go for a walk; as had been recommended to him by some medical quack. One time, on a convalescent trip, I saw him with an eye diagnostician, who gave him self-prepared medicines and massaged him. I could not understand that at the time because the man made an impression on me of being extremely crude. All these cures, as far as I can understand, did not have one definite result. On trips and apart from the stringent official existence, his personality was somewhat loosened, and his health apparently much improved. He loved long walks, which he preferred to take alone, and sports in which he distinguished himself by especially good form. His health grew gradually worse, rather than better, without anyone knowing just exactly what was wrong with him. The colic became more frequent, and he had to have an injection occasionally in order to be able to bear the pain.

"Herr Hess laid particular stress on exactness and good form in his work. When things occurred with which he was not satisfied, he never, as far as I can remember, expressed his dissatisfaction vocally. He was always polite and chivalrous to us ladies. I have often thought to myself how much better he would feel if he would express his anger just once. He always buries his large and small annoyances within himself, and it is probably for this reason that he, in his noble attitude and inner decency, was unable to defend himself against those who handled things ruthlessly. Later he often had difficulties because of his failing health. His old determination failed him, and his ability to concentrate was impaired. One was able to see him day-dreaming in front of his desk for long periods, a situation that was formerly unknown. Possibly this was during the period in which he was making the first preparations for his flight to England, but I am not sure about that.

"Among the people in the Party and among his staff, he was loved and honoured because of his exemplary attitude, with the possible exception of those persons whose nature was so diametrically opposed to his that they were unable or unwilling to identify with this more finely organised individual.

"The fact of his flight to England produced great disturbances and unrest among the people who did not know his reasons. Those men who knew Rudolf Hess were able immediately to evaluate this deed for what it really was. It is characteristic of the man Rudolf Hess that, in his fanatic love for the fatherland, he wanted to make the greatest sacrifice of which he was capable to Adolf Hitler and the German people, namely, to leave nothing undone to bring the German people the dearly desired peace with England and, thereby, to risk his life, his family, his freedom and his honourable name."

CHAPTER X

It was clear from the time of his arrival in Nuremberg that Rudolf Hess was about to present an awkward medico-legal problem for the Tribunal.

Major Kelley's report on his psychiatric status made on October 16th, 1945, to the U.S. authorities, which is referred to in the preceding chapter, made the situation clear. In that report he asked for permission to employ narco-analytic methods of investigation, but this suggestion was turned down by the security branch for reasons very similar to those felt by the Foreign Office in Britain on a much earlier occasion.

Mr. Justice Jackson, U.S. Chief of Counsel, had been fully aware of the peculiar psychiatric problems that might present themselves, not only in the case of Hess, but also in regard to certain of the other defendants. There had in consequence been some discussion on the advisability of a thorough examination in two phases: (1) before trial, to assess fitness to plead and similar matters; and (2) after sentence, when it was felt that a team of psychiatrists, psychologists and sociologists from each of the Allied countries might produce a complete survey and report on these men which would be of value for the future understanding of the Nazi mentality and the nature of the movement which had led to so great disasters. This clearly fitted in well with the expressed hope of the Tribunal that they would write an effective chapter in history.

Phase 1 of this plan was put into operation in November, 1945. On November 8th, Dr. Rees saw the British War Crimes Executive in London, at their request. He was told he was nominated to be asked to go out to Nuremberg. A later telegram asked, however, for an eminent physician and a neurologist to go also, as the Soviet consultant delegation had been so constituted. It was clearly preferable to refer this to the Royal College of Physicians for names, and this was done. Lord Moran and Dr. George Riddoch completed the party, which left on November 12th. Because of bad weather and a very slow and tiresome journey both ways, the stay in Nuremberg was less than twenty-four hours in duration, and the time for consultation and discussion with our colleagues was short.

Colonel Schroeder and our three Russian colleagues were already there—Professor Delay arrived from Paris just before we left. Professors Lewis and Cameron did not arrive from U.S. till a day or two later.

On November 14th, having given the Russian physicians and Col. Schroeder as much insight into the past history as time permitted, we had a group interview with Hess. He sat at one side of a large table with his right hand handcuffed to a U.S. soldier, one evidence of the constant and very proper suicide precautions that were taken by the prison authorities. The visiting commission sat around the other three sides of the table. Since Dr. Rees was the only visitor who was known to Hess, it was arranged that he should come in last, approaching from the door behind the prisoner, so that the meeting of the two could be fully observed by the rest of the group, and thus provide evidence of Hess's recollection of an unexpected face very well known to him for over four years. A courteous greeting and handshake from Dr. Rees produced absolutely no flicker of recognition from Hess, so far as any of the commission or of the prison staff could observe. His manner, while slightly anxious, was apparently exactly what would be expected with a total stranger.

Dr. Rees proceeded to a series of questions and references to events and places in the defendant's recent experience in England, but again met with a blank expression of complete ignorance. It is possibly significant that after two or three minutes of replying to these questions in good English, as he always had done in Britain, Hess suddenly said in German that he could only comprehend if remarks were made to him in German through the interpreter, and from then he spoke only in German throughout the interview. This may of course have been due to anxiety engendered by the considerable group of the commission sitting in front of him, but it would seem more likely that he used the fact that with a patchy or partial amnesia he would be less likely to be questioned so closely through an interpreter, and that he would also have more time to think about his replies. At the time it certainly gave the feeling that it was a defensive move to cover what he felt was a rather weak case.

Many questions were asked and some very tricky sequences of interrogations were put to him by our Russian colleagues and particularly by Col. Schroeder, who has had very extensive medico-legal experience in Chicago. Little was found, however, to disprove or discredit the amnesia. Unlike his blank ignorance when referred to most things in the past, he appeared to accept without question the concept of the Fuehrer and to remember a certain amount about him. Actually this had also been noted in the earlier amnesic attack in Britain, and it almost seemed that Hitler, like God, had in some curious way escaped the oblivion of most men and events in Hess's past life.

Neither on this occasion, nor later when he was seen again and interrogated by the Russian, French and American psychiatrists, was it possible to "break down" the amnesia. It was, however, clear that it was only partial. Certainly it was not so complete as it had been in the previous year in Wales and probably it would vary with circumstance. We knew at this time that in this particular amnesia, just before leaving Wales to come to Nuremberg, his memory had at times been quite good —so good in fact that Dr. Ellis Jones felt confident that this second attack was simulated. In those last months at Abergavenny, he was among men he knew well, the war was over and for the moment the secondary gain of amnesia, of which he had always been quite conscious, would not be so obvious. At Nuremberg in the early days there was clearly a big secondary gain from his symptoms. Neither his defence counsel, nor Goering, with whom he had been allowed to have long talks, were able to find any way through to a recovery of memory. Hess was able to answer many of the commission's questions by reference to things which Goering had told him a few days previously.

On this day in Nuremberg Hess seemed more cadaverous and had clearly lost weight. His photographs taken at the prison make this plain. Unfortunately no photographs of him were ever taken in Great Britain. A careful physical examination revealed little of note in the way of disease or abnormality.

In the consultation which followed, one of the members of the commission felt that Hess's symptoms and disability were so marked that they made him unfit to stand his trial, since he could not challenge witnesses, and that a direct negative reply should be given to the question posed by the Tribunal. The other six of us were by no means in agreement with this, however. There seemed every likelihood that Hess's amnesia would yield once the trial had begun. There were at that time no evidences at all of mental abnormality other than the loss of memory and he was certainly able to comprehend the proceedings.

A somewhat hastily drawn up form of report which includes phrases emphasised by our Russian colleagues was agreed upon by six of us. That document is in the Appendix, Report I (page 217), which was sent through from London word for word as agreed upon by us at Nuremberg. Translation was clearly necessary before the Russian members could deliberate and sign the report, but Report IV (page 223) is their slightly amplified version of it which includes the whole of Report I. United States psychiatrists and Professor Delay from France reported in exactly similar terms (Report II, page 218).

Our colleagues who stayed on after we had had to leave used their opportunities well and were able to amplify their reports somewhat. Especially noteworthy is Report III (page 219), which was put in to the Tribunal by Professor Krasnushkin and his two colleagues as an addition to their shorter report. This is a very valuable document, which obviously might have been made the basis for one single full report signed by everyone, had there been less difficulty over the time-table of arrivals and departures.

One further report is referred to (page 148) in the course the court proceedings. This is not reproduced because it adds nothing to this book, but it was a revised and amplified version of Report I, setting out the same facts and phraseology, but rather more fully, which Dr. Rees and Dr. Riddoch prepared and sent through from England. They had this same feeling as their colleagues in Nuremberg, that the hastily-prepared agreed report could be improved upon quite easily.

The significant point in this whole episode is the final unanimity of judgment of the commission, and the correctness of their guess that the amnesia would break down during the proceedings of the trial.

Watching the trial through the newspaper reports from Nuremberg was somewhat tantalising for those of us who were in Britain. Hess's periodic cramps, for which he had to retire from court, were to be expected. His constant reading of novels and the assumption of indifference to the proceedings which was consistently reported was interesting. This was certainly out of character, for not only had Hess latterly in Wales shown a lively interest in the prospect of the trial, but he had also a considerable regard for the public courtesies in behaviour. To us therefore this conduct seemed to indicate a more conscious note, probably protective, than anything which had been obvious before. It did not require great prescience to foresee that the process of mental dissociation would be reversed.

CHAPTER XI

THE TRIBUNAL AT WORK

On November 30th, 1945, the question whether Hess was fit to stand his trial and to plead was brought before the Tribunal at Nuremberg. The legal arguments based upon the medical evidence given in the reports (quoted in the Appendix) are of considerable interest and the official record of the Nuremberg Tribunal is consequently quoted here in full. The President of the Tribunal was Lord Justice Lawrence from Great Britain.

Various small errors in translation and the transcription of the original document have been left untouched and are reproduced here.

THE PRESIDENT: I call upon counsel for the defendant Hess.

DR. VON ROHRSCHEIDT (*counsel for the defendant Hess*): May it please the Tribunal, I am speaking here as counsel for the defendant Rudolf Hess.

The proceedings which have already been opened against Hess—the court has to decide on the question whether the defendant is capable of being heard or not, and also whether the conditions are present which would make him entirely irresponsible.

Personally, the court has laid down these juristic principles in the opinion, and has asked those who are expressing their opinion—the experts—to say whether, firstly, the defendant is in a state in which he can plead against the charge; secondly, about his mental stability. And the question here was formulated as to whether the defendant is mentally sound or not.

In respect to question 1, is the defendant in a fit state to plead, the Tribunal has asked the experts certain questions as to whether the defendant is sufficiently in possession of his mental faculties in order to understand the proceedings, and whether an adequate defence can be undertaken, that is, whether he can understand evidence given.

The experts to whom this task was entrusted have examined Hess on several different days and given their expert opinion to the Tribunal. I as his defence counsel must, because it is my duty, after having studied these experts' opinions—I couldn't do it sufficiently thoroughly because time was short—I personally, after having looked at these documents, and in conjunction with my experience with defendant Hess in almost daily discussions, am of the opinion that the defendant is not capable of pleading.

I therefore consider it my duty and I feel forced to make the following application:

Firstly, I should ask that the proceedings against Hess be temporarily quashed; secondly, in case his inability to plead should be admitted by the Tribunal, I should request the Tribunal not to carry out the proceedings if the defendant is not there. But in case the Tribunal should consider Hess fit to plead, I should ask for an arbitral expert opinion in order to decide the question.

Before I come to the reasons for my application, I should like to say on behalf of the defendant that he, Hess himself, thinks he is fit to plead and would like to tell the court so himself.

I would now like to give the reasons for my application:

If my defendant—my client, rather—should not be fit to plead, I should like the proceedings against Hess to be temporarily quashed.

I should like to refer to the opinions already submitted to the Tribunal. The experts come to the following result—I should like to call one of them the main expert. This was given by English, Soviet and American experts, bearing the date of November 15th, 1945. I should like to cite textually from this. In this opinion it is said that the capacity of the defendant Hess is reduced. That is to say, his capacity to defend himself and to face a witness and to understand the evidence. I have cited this formulation because it is closest to the question put to the experts by the Tribunal.

The opinion says that even if Hess's amnesia does not prevent the defendant from understanding what is going on about him and to follow the proceedings in court——

THE PRESIDENT (*interposing*): Would you speak a little more slowly? The interpreters are not able to interpret so fast.

Would you also refer us especially to those parts of the medical reports to which you wish to draw our attention?

Do you understand what I said?

DR. VON ROHRSCHEIDT: Yes.

I should like to observe that I haven't got the exact quotations according to the pages of the English text, as I only have the German translation, so I can only do it as I have just said.

The first quotation—

THE PRESIDENT (*interposing*): You can read the words in German, and they will be translated into English.

Which report are you referring to?

DR. VON ROHRSCHEIDT: For the quotation that I gave I was referring to the expert opinion which was given on November 14th, 1945, which was drawn up by the English, Soviet and American delegations, and which included the report of the 17th of November, 1945. What I quoted was the following —may I repeat it?

The passage runs: "The capability of the defendant Hess is reduced in respect of being able to defend himself, to face a witness, and to understand the details of the evidence given."

THE PRESIDENT: Can you say which of the doctors you are quoting?

DR. VON ROHRSCHEIDT: It is the report which, in my copy, is dated the November 14th, 1945, and, as I said, was presumably signed by Soviet, American and English doctors.

Unfortunately, the original copy I did not receive again yesterday evening after I had given it back. That is, I was not able to obtain the original again.

THE PRESIDENT: Have the English prosecutors got a copy, and can you tell us which it is?

SIR DAVID MAXWELL-FYFE: I think I am in the same difficulties as your Lordship. I have copies of four medical reports. At the end of the document headed "Order", it says, "Copies of four medical reports are attached".

The first one of these is signed by three English doctors on the 19th of November.

The second is signed by three American and a French doctor, dated November 20th.

There is a report signed by three Soviet doctors, dated the November 17th.

There is one signed by three Soviet doctors and the French doctor dated November 16th.

These are the only ones which I have with the Court's order.

F

THE PRESIDENT: Yes.

I don't know what this report is that you are referring to.

SIR DAVID MAXWELL-FYFE: Dr. von Rohrscheidt seems to have an unsigned report of the 14th.

THE PRESIDENT: Dr. von Rohrscheidt, have you got the four reports which are really before us? I will read them out to you:

The first one I have got in my hand is November 19th, 1945, by Lord Moran, Dr. Rees and Dr. Riddoch. Have you got that? That is the English report.

DR. VON ROHRSCHEIDT: I only have this report in the German translation and not in the original.

THE PRESIDENT: But if you have got it in the German translation, that is quite good enough.

Then the next one is dated the 20th of November, 1945, by Dr. Delay, Dr. Nolan Lewis, Dr. Cameron and Colonel Paul Schroeder.

Have you got that?

DR. VON ROHRSCHEIDT: Yes, I have that one.

THE PRESIDENT: That is two.

Then, the next one is dated November 16th, and is signed by three Soviet doctors and one French doctor, Dr. Delay, dated 16th of November. Have you got that?

Then there is another report of the 17th, signed by the three Soviet doctors alone, without the French doctor.

Now, will you refer to the passages in those reports upon which you rely?

There is another report by the two English doctors which is practically the same. That is the one I have already referred to, that does not contain the name of Lord Moran on it, dated the 19th of November.

DR. VON ROHRSCHEIDT: May the Tribunal please, I think I can shorten this speech to the Tribunal. My view is that all the experts' opinions agree that the capability of the defendant Hess to defend himself, to face a witness, and to understand the details of the evidence given—perhaps I should keep exactly to these words in my exposition:

If we assume that all the medical opinions are agreed that the defendant Hess is reduced in his capacity for defence, I should, in my capacity as his defence counsel, be convinced that the ability to plead of the defendant Hess should be negatived. The reduction of the capability of the defendant in his defence, which is recognised as a mental defect, as amnesia, recognised by all the experts, shows a mental condition of a mixed kind but anyhow a mental defect, so he should not be considered as fit to plead.

I am of the opinion that this statement made by the medical experts shows, as was stated in the question to the experts, that on account of this mental defect, the amnesia, proper defence for the defendant Hess is not possible. The opinions also assume that the defendant is not actually insane. That is not the important point at the moment because according to the medical opinion it is affirmatively stated, in my opinion, that the defendant is not in a condition to follow everything in consequence of the reduction of his mental capacity.

I personally—and I think my own opinion agrees with the medical opinion—think that the defendant is quite incapable of making himself understood to the extent that one would expect from a mentally normal person, to the extent that one would expect and demand from a mentally normal person.

I consider that the defendant—I am basing this on my own experience with him—is not capable of understanding what the Tribunal says to him in such a manner as is necessary for his defence because his memory is very unreliable. Through his loss of memory he knows neither events which have happened in the past nor the persons who were associated with him in the past. I therefore am of the opinion that the opposite opinion of the defendant himself, namely, that he is fit to plead, is irrelevant. As the reduction of the defendant's capacity, according to medical opinion, will not soon be improved, I am therefore of the opinion that the proceedings against defendant Hess should be quashed.

Whether the treatment proposed by the medical experts, by narcotic analysis, would bring improvement is not certain, nor in what way nor at what time the health of the defendant can be restored. The medical opinions reproach the defendant with refusing to have such medical treatment. The defendant tells me, on the contrary, that he would be ready to undergo such treatment, but he refused the treatment in this case because, first of all, he thinks he is already fit to plead and therefore considers such a cure unnecessary, also because he is an opponent of such forceful methods, and finally because he is of the opinion that such forced operation just at this time might make him unfit to plead, that is to say, would rather exclude him from the proceedings, which is just what he wishes to avoid.

If the defendant is not capable of pleading, incapable of defending himself, as medical opinion says, and if this state is likely to last for a long time, this would be a condition for temporary suspension of the proceedings against him.

My second application: In case the Tribunal should allow my application and declare the defendant Hess unfit to plead, then, according to Article 12 of the Charter, it is possible to proceed against the defendant in absentia. Section 12 provides that the Tribunal has the right to proceed against a defendant in his absence if he cannot be found, or if this is in the interests of justice or other reasons. Is it then in the interests of justice to proceed against the defendant in absentia? In my opinion, it is not in accordance with objective justice if actual proofs are available, as they are here, that the defendant's capacity is reduced because of illness and he is hindered in defending himself personally.

Such terrible crimes are laid at the door of the defendant that even the death penalty is to be expected. It is therefore incompatible with objective justice if medical experts say he is not capable of defending himself. And according to Paragraph 12 of the Charter, this right in Paragraph 16 of the Charter provides for a defence and also the possibility of bringing personal evidence for his defence, and cross-examining any witness, and this is most important for the defence and any exclusion of such a possibility is, in my opinion, not right. Proceedings in absentia would preclude all this, and therefore could not be considered just.

If the defendant is reduced in his capacity to defend himself, for the reasons already stated, to such a degree then the defendant is not in a position to give his counsel the necessary information and then to put his counsel in a position to defend him in his absence.

As the Charter has so precisely laid down the rights of the defendants to form their own defence, it seems to me as defence counsel unjust to deprive the defendant of these rights because he is hindered by reasons of illness from being there. The possibility of carrying out proceedings in absentia against a defendant must surely be looked upon as an exception which should only be applied against a defendant if he wishes to avoid the proceedings. But defendant Hess has told me and emphasised to me, and he will probably do it to the Tribunal, that he wishes to attend the proceedings, and he will certainly feel it is particularly unjust if he were ready to plead and should be excluded and the proceedings were carried out in absentia.

I therefore request the Tribunal, if it should declare the defendant not competent to plead, that it shall not proceed in his absence.

Now, one more application: if the Tribunal, against my own opinion and against the opinion which, in my view, is expressed in the medical statements, should consider he is fit to plead, I should ask for one more medical opinion and that this question may be investigated once more, because I have seen from the medical statements already available that the experts have only spoken with Hess for a short time, in one case only for two days, and in any case for a very short period. In a case of such world-wide importance it seems to me necessary that a complete picture should be given. For this longer examination would be necessary, perhaps in a suitable hospital, and that he be observed for weeks at a time. The experts themselves are obviously not quite sure whether the defendant Hess is mentally ill, even beyond what is admitted; that is, not capable of pleading that he is mentally deficient. This opinion I have gained because all the medical statements emphasise that the accused is not considered fit to plead, that he should be again subjected to a psychiatric examination. I think this suggestion should be followed in accordance with the suggestion made by the psychiatrists who have already examined him. I should therefore plead, if the Tribunal should consider the defendant fit to plead, that the suggestion of psychiatrists should be followed and that another opinion should be taken.

THE PRESIDENT: I want to ask you one question: Is it not consistent with all the medical opinions that the defendant is capable of understanding the course of the proceedings, and that the only illness from which he is suffering is his forgetfulness about what happened before he flew to England?

DR. VON ROHRSCHEIDT: Mr. President, it is true that the

experts say that the defendant Hess is capable of following the proceedings. That is true. But they emphasise, on the other hand, that the defendant is not capable of defending himself. In the manner in which the questions were put to the experts, the Tribunal asked the experts to state their views on the following: Is the defendant mentally sound or not? This question is answered by all experts in the affirmative, that he is mentally sound. But that does not exclude the fact that the defendant might at the moment be incapable of pleading and in this respect the experts again, referring to the questions put to them—the Tribunal would like to know whether the defendant is capable of following the course of the proceedings, can he carry out adequate defence as a witness and understand the evidence?

And there I am of the opinion that the experts, keeping to the question, give the answer that the defendant is not capable of carrying out an adequate defence, to put objections to the witness, or to follow the details of the evidence given. That is, I consider, contained in all the experts' opinions.

Looking at the opinion given by the French and American delegations, if I may submit that to the Court, the date 20th of November, "as a result of our said investigations, we find that Hess is suffering from hysteria and loss of memory". Now comes this passage: "The loss of memory is of such a kind that it will not disturb his understanding of the proceedings, but in respect to questions about his past, he will not respond and that would reduce the weight of his defence. Therefore the capability of the accused for defence is reduced."

So from that he should be considered as not fit to plead. And in the medical opinion of the French delegation, signed by Professor Delay, that too says that the defendant can understand everything that goes on around him, but that his amnesia has such an effect on his capability of carrying out his defence, and to understand all the details which refer to his past, that these facts must be looked upon as disturbing. I considered that if one interprets these statements as the experts intended, the experts mean that the defendant is not insane, he can follow the proceedings, but he cannot defend himself because he is suffering from a credible amnesia.

THE TRIBUNAL (Judge Biddle): Do you accept the opinion of the experts?

Dr. von Rohrscheidt: Yes.

The Tribunal (General Nikitchenko): I should like to know the translation. I should like to draw the attention of the defence that he is incorrectly referring to the experts' opinion of the Soviet experts and French expert. Very good translating; not quite correctly. It was a free translation.

Dr. von Rohrscheidt: May I read to the Tribunal what my translation says? The translation was made here in the Bureau and was given to me in this translation. May I repeat that the translation in my possession refers to November 16th, 1945, and was signed by the members of the Soviet delegation and Professor Delay in Paris.

Sub-number three:

"At the present moment the defendant is not insane in the strict sense of the word. His amnesia does not prevent him from following everything that is going on around him. But it affects his capability of carrying out the defence and of remembering all details of the past, and might be disturbing."

The President: That is all we wish to ask you. Does the Chief Prosecutor for the United States wish to address the Tribunal?

Mr. Justice Jackson: I think General Rudenko would like to open discussion, if that is agreeable.

The President: Yes. Are you going on?

General Rudenko: In connection with the statement made by the defence, and as a result of the doctor's opinion, I am inclined to say the following: The condition of Hess was examined by experts. These experts appointed by the Tribunal have agreed that Hess is sane and can answer for his actions. The Chief Prosecutors have discussed the results of this according to the orders of the Tribunal and have answered the question of the Tribunal as follows:

One, we have no questions and doubts about the Commission's report. We are of opinion that Hess can be tried.

That is the opinion of the Prosecutors. We are finding that the terms stated by the experts, that Hess can be considered sane——

The President (interposing): Will you speak more slowly please?

General Rudenko: We considered that the experts'

opinions are quite sufficient for carrying on the decision of the Tribunal to find Hess sane and subject to this Court, and we are asking the Tribunal to sign accordingly the following statement; and the defence is asking to postpone the proceedings in view of his illness and state. I must say that defence is citing—I don't know why, not quite correctly. It is stated here by the defence that Hess is not able and he is in such condition that he cannot defend himself and understand witnesses, and so on.

It is quite differently stated by the experts. The experts state that Hess is suffering from amnesia and it will not completely affect him in understanding the proceedings. It certainly won't interfere with his understanding of the witnesses. I think that the details of the past period, which Hess probably will not remember, will not interest the Tribunal. The main points which the experts have given in their reports, and which we do not doubt, and which don't raise any doubts by the defence, is that Hess is sane, and if he is sane Hess must be tried, and according to this I consider that the request of the defence should be refused.

SIR DAVID MAXWELL-FYFE: May it please the Tribunal:

It has been suggested that I might say just a word, and as shortly as the Tribunal desire, as to the legal conceptions which govern the position with which the Tribunal and this defendant are placed at the present time.

The question before the Tribunal is whether this defendant is able to plead to the Indictment and should be tried at the present time.

If I might very briefly refer the Tribunal to the short passages in the report, which I submit are relevant, it might be useful at the present time. According to the attachments to the Order, which I have, the first report is that signed by the British doctors on November 19th, 1945. And in that report I beg the Tribunal to refer to Paragraph 3, in which the signatories say: "At the moment he is not insane in the strict sense. His loss of memory will not entirely interfere with his comprehension of the proceedings, but it will interfere with his ability to make his defence, and to understand details of the past, which arise in evidence."

The next report is that signed by the American and French doctors, and in Paragraph 1 the Tribunal will see: "We find, as a result of our examinations and investigations, that Rudolf Hess is suffering from hysteria characterised in part by loss of memory. The nature of this loss of memory is such that it will not interfere with his comprehension of the proceedings, but it will interfere with his response to questions relating to his past and will interfere with his undertaking his defence."

If the Tribunal will proceed to the third report, signed by the Soviet doctors, at the foot of page 1, of the copy that I have, there is a paragraph beginning "Psychologically——" which I submit is of importance—"Psychologically, Hess is in a state of clear consciousness; knows that he is imprisoned at Nürnberg under indictment as a war criminal; has read and, according to his own words, is acquainted with the charges against him. He answers questions rapidly and to the point. His speech is coherent, his thoughts formed with precision and correctness and they are accompanied by sufficient emotionally expressive movements. Also, there is no kind of evidence of paranoia. It should also be noted here that the present psychological examinations, which were conducted by Lt. Gilbert, Doctor of Medicine, and of the testimony, is that the intelligence of Hess is normal and in some instances above average. His movements are natural and not forced."

Now, if I may come to the next report, I am sorry—the report which is signed by the three Soviet doctors and Professor Delay of Paris, dated the 16th, which is the last in my bundle, and that says in Paragraph 3:

"At present he is not insane in the strict sense of the word. His amnesia does not prevent him completely from understanding what is going on around him, but it will interfere with his ability to conduct his defence and to understand details of the past which would appear as factual data."

I refer, without quoting, because I do not consider that they are of sufficient importance on this point, to the explanation of the kind and reason of the amnesia which appeared in the Soviet report, dated November 17th, under the numbers One, Two and Three, at the end of the report. But I remind the Tribunal that all these reports unite in saying that there is no form of insanity.

In these circumstances, the question in English law, and I respectfully submit that to the consideration of the Tribunal as

F*

being representative of natural justice in this regard, is, in deciding whether the defendant is fit to plead, whether the defendant be insane or not, and the time which is relevant for the deciding of that issue is at the date of the arraignment and not at any prior time.

Different views have been expressed as to the party on whom the onus of proof lies in that issue, but the latter, and logically the better view, is that the onus is on the defendant, because it is always presumed that a person is sane until the contrary is proved.

Now, if I might refer the Court to one case which I suspect, if I may so use my mind, has not been absent from the Court's mind, because of the wording of the notice which we are discussing to-day, it is the case of Pritchard in 7 Carrington and Pike, which is referred to in Archbold, Criminal Pleading, in the 1943 edition, at page 147:

In Pritchard's case, where a prisoner arraigned on an indictment for felony appeared to be deaf, dumb, and also of non-sane mind, Baron Alderson put three distinct issues to the jury, directing the jury to be sworn separately on each: Whether the prisoner was mute, of malice, or by the visitation of God; (2) Whether he was able to plead; (3) Whether he was sane or. not. And on the last issue they were directed to inquire whether the prisoner was of sufficient intellect to comprehend the course of the proceedings of the trial so as to make a proper defence, to challenge a juror, that is, a member of the jury, to whom he might wish to object and to understand the details of the evidence; and he directed the jury that if there was no certain mode of communicating to the prisoner the details of the evidence so that he could clearly understand them, and be able properly to make his defence to the charge against him, the jury ought to find that he was not of sane mind.

I submit to the Tribunal that the words there quoted, "to comprehend the course of the proceedings of the trial so as to make a proper defence," emphasise that the material time, the only time which should be considered, is whether at the moment of plea and of trial the defendant understands his charge against him and the evidence by which it is supported.

THE PRESIDENT: And does not relate to his memory at that time.

Sir David Maxwell-Fyfe: That is, I respectfully agree with your Lordship, it does not relate to his memory. It has never, in English jurisprudence, to my knowledge, been held to be a bar either to trial or punishment, that a person who comprehends the charge and the evidence has not got a memory as to what happened at the time. That, of course, is entirely a different course which does not arise either on these reports or of this application.

As to what was the defendant's state of mind, no one here suggests that the defendant's state of mind and the action charged were committed was abnormal, and it does not come into this case.

The President: He will, it seems to me, be able to put forward his amnesia as part of his defence.

Sir David Maxwell-Fyfe: Certainly my Lord.

The President: And to say: "I should have been able to make a better defence if I had been able to remember what took place at the time."

Sir David Maxwell-Fyfe: Yes, sir. If I might compare a very simple case within my experience, and I am sure within the experience of members of the Court where this has arisen scores of times, in English courts, after a motor accident when a man is charged with manslaughter or doing grievous bodily harm, he is often in the position of saying, "because of the accident my memory is not good, or fails as to the exact charge". No one has even suggested that it could be a matter of relief from criminal responsibility. I hope that the Tribunal will not think that I have occupied too much of their time, but I thought it was useful just to present the matter on the basis of the English law as I understand it.

The Tribunal (Mr. Biddle): So I can understand you, one of the tests under the Pritchard case is whether or not the defendant can make a proper defence?

Sir David Maxwell-Fyfe: With the greatest respect, will the doctor read the preceding words. They say: "Whether the prisoner was of sufficient intellect to comprehend the course of the proceedings of the trial so as to make a proper defence."

The Tribunal (Mr. Biddle): And would you interpret that to mean that this defendant could make a proper defence under the procedure of the trial if you also find it a fact, which you I think do not dispute, and which you quoted in fact, that although not insane—now I quote: "He did not understand, or rather his amnesia does not prevent him completely from understanding, what is going on around him but it will interfere with his ability to conduct his defence, and understand details of the past." You don't think that is inconsistent with that finding?

SIR DAVID MAXWELL-FYFE: I am submitting it is not. It is part of his defence, and it may well be "I don't remember anything about that at all". And he could actually say "from my general behaviour or from other acts which I undoubtedly have done, it is extremely unlikely that I should do it". That is the defence which is left to him. And he must take that defence, and it is my submission.

THE TRIBUNAL (Mr. Biddle): So even if we assume for the purpose of argument that his amnesia is complete, and that he remembers nothing that occurred before the indictment, though not understanding the proceedings, you think he should be tried?

SIR DAVID MAXWELL-FYFE: I submit he should be tried. That is my submission as a legal position. I especially didn't discuss—of course the Tribunal will appreciate that—I didn't discuss the quantum of amnesia here because I am not putting that to the Tribunal; I wanted to put before the Tribunal the legal basis on which this application is posed. Therefore I accept readily the extreme case which the learned American judge put to me.

THE TRIBUNAL (Mr. DeVabres): I ask in what period the real amnesia of Hess applies. He pretends to have forgotten facts which occurred more than fifteen days ago. It may be simulation or, as they say in the report, it may be real simulation. I would like to know if according to the reports Hess has really lost his memory of facts which are referred to in the Indictment.

SIR DAVID MAXWELL-FYFE: The facts which are included in the Indictment, the explanations that the doctors give as to his amnesia, are most clearly set out in these paragraphs of the Soviet report, that is the third report dated November 17th, 1945, page two, and the numbered paragraphs one to three. They say first:

"In the psychological personality of Hess there are no changes typical of the progressive schizophrenic disease." That is, there are no changes typical of a progressive double personality developing from which he suffered periodically while in England; (I am sorry) "therefore the delusions from which he suffered periodically while in England cannot be considered as manifestations of a schizophrenic paranoia, and must be recognised as the expression of a psychogenic paranoiac reaction, that is, the psychologically comprehensible reaction—"

Now I ask the learned French judge to note the next sentence: "Of an unstable personality to the situation (the failure of his mission, arrest and incarceration). Such is the interpretation of the delirious statements of Hess in England as bespoken by the disappearance, appearance and repeated disappearance depending on external circumstances which affected the mental state of Hess."

Paragraph two: "The loss of memory by Hess is not the result of some kind of mental disease, but represents hysterical amnesia, the basis of which is a subconscious inclination towards self-defence." Now I ask the learned French judge to note again the next words: "As well as a deliberate and conscious tendency towards it. Such behaviour often terminates when the hysterical person is faced with an unavoidable necessity of conducting himself correctly. Therefore the amnesia of Hess may end upon his being brought to trial.

Three: "Rudolf Hess, prior to his flight to England, did not suffer from any kind of insanity, nor is he now suffering from it. At the present time he exhibits hysterical behaviour with signs of"—and again I ask the learned French judge to note this point —"with signs of a conscious-intentional (simulated) character which does not exonerate him from his responsibility under the Indictment."

The last sentence is a matter for the Tribunal. But in these circumstances it would be impossible to say that the amnesia may continue to be complete or is entirely unconscious. That is deliberately avoided by the learned doctors. Therefore the prosecution do not say that that is the case, but they do say that even if it were complete, the legal basis which I have suggested to the Court is a correct one for action in the matter.

THE PRESIDENT: Thank you, Sir David. Would Doctor Rohrscheidt like to add anything by way of reply? One moment; Mr. Justice Jackson, I gathered from what Sir David said that he was speaking on behalf of you and of the French prosecution, is that correct?

JUSTICE JACKSON: I intend to adopt all that he said. I would only add a few more words, if I may.

THE PRESIDENT: Doctor Rohrscheidt, Mr. Justice Jackson has something to say first of all.

JUSTICE JACKSON: I adopt all that has been said, and will not repeat. We have three applications before the Tribunal. One is for another examination. I will spend very little time on that. I think we have made, up to this point with these examinations, medical history in having seven psychiatrists from five nations who are completely in agreement. An achievement of that kind is not likely to be risked.

The only reason suggested here is that a relatively short time has been devoted to the examination, but I suggest to your Honours that that is not the situation, because there have been available the examinations and observations and medical history during the incarceration of Hess in England, extending from 1941, and the reports of the psychiatrists of the American Forces since he was brought to Nürnberg, and they all agree. So that there is a more complete medical history in this case than in most cases.

The next application was as to trial in absentia. I shall spend no time on that, for there seems to be no occasion for trying Hess in absentia if he shouldn't be tried in his presence. If he is unable to be tried, why he simply shouldn't be tried at all. That is all I can see to it.

I would like to call your attention to the one thing in all this, the one thing, on which any case can be made here for postponement. That is the statement with which we all agree: That Hess's condition will interfere with his response to questions relating to his past and will interfere with his undertaking his defence. Now, I think it will interfere with his defence if he persists in it, and I am sure that counsel has a very difficult task. But Hess has refused the treatment, and I have filed with the court the report of Major Kelley, the American psychiatrist, in whose care he was placed immediately after he was brought here.

He has refused every single treatment that has been suggested. He has refused to submit to the ordinary things that we submit to every day, blood tests, examinations, and says he will submit to nothing until after the trial. The medication which was suggested to bring him out of this hysterical situation—every psychiatrist agrees that this is simply a hysterical situation if it is genuine at all—was the use of intravenous drugs of the barbital series, either sodium amytal or sodium phenotal, the ordinary sedative that you perhaps take on a sleepless night. We did not dare administer that, to be perfectly candid, against his objection, because we felt that however harmless—and in over a thousand cases observed by Major Kelley there has been no ill effect although some cases are reported where there has— we felt that if he should be struck by lightning a month afterward it would still be charged that something that we had done had caused his death; and we did not desire to impose any such treatment upon him.

But I respectfully suggest that a man cannot stand afar from the Court and assert that his amnesia is a defence to his being tried, and at the same time refuse the simple medical expedients which we all agree might be useful.

He is in the volunteer class with his amnesia. In England, as the reports show, he is reported to have made the statement that his earlier amnesia was simulated. He came out of this state during a period in England, then went back to it. It is now highly selective. That is to say, you can't be sure what Hess will remember and what he will not remember. His amnesia is not of the type which is a complete blotting out of the personality, of the type that would be fatal to his defence.

So we feel that so long as Hess refuses the ordinary, simple expedients, even if his amnesia is genuine, that he is not in a position to continue to assert that he must not be brought to trial. We think he should be tried, not in absentia but in these proceedings.

THE TRIBUNAL (Mr. Biddle): Isn't Hess asserting that he wants to be tried?

JUSTICE JACKSON: Well, I don't know about that. He has been interrogated and interrogated by us, as have the co-defendants, and I wouldn't attempt to say what he would now say he wants. I haven't observed that it is causing him any great distress. Frankly, I doubt very much if he would like to be absent, but I wouldn't attempt to speak for him.

THE PRESIDENT: Does Mr. Dobost wish to add anything?

DR. ROHRSCHEIDT: May I just say a few words to the Tribunal to make my point of view clear once more?

As defence counsel of the defendant Hess this is my point of view. First, factually, the defendant Hess, according to the reports of the doctors which all agree, has a mental defect.

Secondly, the accused Hess is suffering from amnesia, which again all medical experts admit exists. This is merely remarked in the report, whether this amnesia is paranoiac or psycho-genetic. They are all agreed that this amnesia is on a patho-logical basis. The result is that the defendant is not insane, but has a mental defect. From that emerges, I think in a legal sense, that the defendant cannot state that he cannot be made responsible for his actions, but presumably, when the deeds were committed he was certainly not mentally insane. But there is a difference, according to German law at any rate, whether the defendant is at the moment in a position to follow the trial, that is, whether he is fit to plead. This question should, in my opinion, as I have already said, on the basis of the medical reports, be negatived. He is not capable of being tried.

The Tribunal may be doubtful of the answers of the experts. It is difficult to understand whether the defendant is actually restricted in his capability of defending himself or whether he can have an adequate defence. I think that possibly this point should be stressed: The loss of memory is affirmed by all the experts, and it would seem to me that he is not capable of making adequate defence.

One other point: He may be able to defend himself, and seem normal externally, he can follow the course of the pro-ceedings, but he cannot defend himself adequately, that is, in the same way as a person who is in full possession of his normal senses.

May I perhaps add one word. I have already explained that the defendant has expressed the wish to me that he would like to attend the trial, as he does not feel himself unfit to plead, but that, in the opinion of the defence, is completely irrelevant.

In respect of the consequences as foreseen by the American prosecutor, that the defendant has refused to be treated by narcotic means, that is not a question of truculence, but he refused because he was afraid that the intravenous injections at this particular moment might, in his weakened state, make him incapable of following the proceedings, which is exactly what he did not want.

I have already mentioned that he himself thinks he is sane, and therefore he did not need any intravenous treatment. The defendant Hess also told me that he has an internal abhorrence of such means, and Hess, in the unhappy times of the National Socialist regime, was always for the natural method of healing. He even founded the Rudolf Hess Hospital in Dresden, which is conducted on natural, not medical, means.

JUSTICE JACKSON: May I make one observation, Your Honours?

THE PRESIDENT: Yes.

JUSTICE JACKSON: The argument illustrates the selectivity of the memory of which I spoke to you. Hess apparently can inform his counsel about his attitude towards this particular matter during the National Socialist regime. His counsel is able to tell us how he felt about medical things during the National Socialist regime, but when we ask him about anything in which he participated that might have a criminal aspect, the memory becomes bad. I hope that the Court has not overlooked the statement of the matters that he does well recollect.

DR. ROHRSCHEIDT: May I make a correction?

THE PRESIDENT: It is unusual to hear counsel in a second reply, but as Mr. Justice Jackson has spoken again we will hear what you have to say.

DR. ROHRSCHEIDT: I would merely like to observe that I was misunderstood. It was not the defendant who told me that he was an adherent of natural medicine, and in such a way proved that he had retained his memory, but it was I who, from my own memory, ascertained this, and I knew that he was. I gave that as my opinion and my experience in order to show that he has an intellectual aversion to medical operations, but this remark was not based on memory of the defendant Hess but on my own memory.

THE PRESIDENT: Dr. Rohrscheidt, the Tribunal would like, if you consider it proper, that the Defendant Hess should state what his views on this question are.

DR. ROHRSCHEIDT: As his defence counsel, I have certainly nothing to say against it, and I think it would be the defendant's own wish, and the Tribunal would then be in a position to judge what mental state the defendant is in. He can speak as to whether he considers himself fit to plead from where he is.

THE DEFENDANT HESS: Mr. President, I would like to say this: At the beginning of the trial of this afternoon's proceedings I gave my defence counsel a note that I am of the opinion that these proceedings could be shortened if one would allow me to speak myself. What I say is as follows:

In order to anticipate any possibility of my being declared incapable of pleading, although I am willing to take part in the rest of the proceedings with the rest of them, I would like to give the Tribunal the following declaration, although I originally intended not to make this declaration until a later point in the proceedings:

My memory is again in order. The reasons why I simulated loss of memory were tactical. In fact, it is only that my capacity for concentration is slightly reduced. But in consequence of that, my capacity to follow the trial, my capacity to defend myself, to put questions to witnesses or even to answer questions —these, my capacities, are not influenced by that.

I emphasise the fact that I bear the full responsibility for everything that I have done or signed as signatory or co-signatory. My attitude, in principle, is that the Tribunal is not competent—is not affected by the statement I have just made. Hitherto in conversations with my official defence counsel I have maintained my loss of memory. He was, therefore, in good faith when he asserted I lost my memory.

THE PRESIDENT: The trial is adjourned.

(Whereupon at 1830 hours the hearing of the Tribunal adjourned to reconvene at 1400 hours on December 1st, 1945).

A few minutes later (probably by 1835 hours, Central European Time) the Radio commentators were busy. In San Francisco and Capetown, in Leeds and in Stockholm, people were saying—"Well, well, so that's that. I knew all along he was malingering. Think of it, seven psychiatrists, two neurologists, and two internists! What a lot of suckers."

CHAPTER XII

THE three American psychiatrists who stayed on for a while in Nuremberg after the Court proceedings were somewhat concerned about the unusual attitude of Hess and about the general evidences of instability which he was displaying. They very rightly put in a report to the Tribunal on the question of his instability, though it is probable that the Court as a group of intelligent laymen had realised that the situation was not all going to be plain sailing.

As a result of this report and the reading of the documents which are reproduced in the last chapter, the journal of the American Medical Association produced a very valuable summary of the situation, stressing a point which has up to date not been sufficiently underlined. The psychiatric procedure by which specialists make their report to the Court rather than to the defence or prosecution is comparatively new to legal circles. In the British Army it has been followed throughout the war so far as psychiatrists were concerned and no army psychiatrist was allowed to be called for either prosecution or defence, but only to make his report direct to those responsible for the court-martial. It is therefore interesting to get this further comment on the obvious wisdom of such a procedure, and part of the brief article is by permission reproduced here, from the journal of the American Medical Association, March 23rd, 1946, p. 790.

"CURRENT COMMENT. PSYCHIATRIC EXAMINATION OF RUDOLF HESS"

"The role of the psychiatrist in the trial of the leading Axis war criminals has attained historical significance. This significance derives in a large measure from the fact that the psychiatric panel was appointed by the International Military Tribunal and reported its findings direct to that body. The panel consisted of three representative Russian psychiatrists, three British, one French and three American."

Here follows a list of the psychiatrists concerned which is given in the Appendix, and a copy of their report (Report II) page 218.

The journal then continues:

"The psychiatrists were permitted to study these defendants as impartial workers utilising the scientific method. The procedure removed the restriction imposed on the expert witness in civilian courts in both criminal and civil trials in that they served neither the prosecution nor the defence. Because such a procedure is well-nigh unique in criminal jurisprudence, it has historical interest. The appointment of psychiatrists from four geographically widely separated countries, speaking three different languages and coming from other cultures, assured a diversity of point of view and breadth of approach. The tribunal did not limit the psychiatrists to direct categorical replies; it authorised a report made in the form which commended itself to the examiners. This is likewise unique in court practice. The hearing of the tribunal on Nov. 30th, 1945, concerning the mental state of the defendant was noteworthy on several counts. First among these is the remarkable degree of accord revealed in the reports of the groups of psychiatric experts representing the four countries responsible for the trial. This essential agreement between the groups, whose examinations, with the exception of that of the French, who participated in all three, were carried out separately, strengthens the conclusions of the psychiatric panel. Within the period of four years his record included a great variety of symptoms, delusions of persecution, two suicidal attempts, two periods of hysterical amnesia, various bodily symptoms such as abdominal cramps, which apparently are of neurotic origin, and finally his last dramatic outburst. These abnormalities of behaviour have appeared and vanished as the pressures to which he has been subjected since he broke away from his established position in the Nazi hierarchy have waxed and waned."

CHAPTER XIII

MAJOR KELLEY takes up the story again:

"On November 30th, immediately after Hess's famous declaration that his memory was now in order, I interviewed him in his cell. He was elated over the impression he had created in the court-room and stated that his memory was now in good shape. He claimed that his memory now extended throughout his entire life, but on persistent questioning indicated that there were still a number of things on which he was not quite clear and for which his memory was still faulty. When asked about the small packages which he had sealed up, he readily recalled them, but emphasised that the action was necessary since the English were definitely trying to weaken him by giving him special medication and had attempted to drive him insane in order to destroy the functioning of his mind and his value to Germany. He was very proud of his acting ability in fooling everyone, and was particularly gratified at his confusing Goering. He did emphasise that the motion picture test was the most difficult and stated that he felt that certain individuals who were constantly with him, like myself, probably were aware that certain of his reactions were false. He admitted considerable fear of me and stated that he considered my observations most dangerous to his scheme. He recalled his stay in England and stated that during this period he had short transitory episodes of true amnesia during which time he had actually forgotten many things. During these periods of actual amnesia he discovered that his interrogators passed over such forgotten matters, and as his memory would return he employed this knowledge in continuing to feign memory loss in order to prevent further questioning. His actual amnesia therefore demonstrated the great value of memory loss to him and it was this that gave him the idea of carrying on his pretence. He felt in England that such total memory loss might cause the British to repatriate him as an insane person. When this failed and he was brought to Nuremberg as a war criminal, he felt that he should maintain his memory loss because it would permit him better to survey the situation and prepare his defence without giving his interrogators a chance to find out anything about him. He also stated that his papers had been taken away from him on arrival and the memory loss had given him a chance to see these papers and parcels, which was of great value to him. At the actual interview, described above, Hess merely gave his documents a cursory glance and the memory loss was of no value at any time in this particular instance.

"Hess recalled very definitely his flight to England, stating that the only people who knew about the event were his two adjutants. He was very proud of his flight, describing it minutely and bragging about his navigational ability. He left in a Messerschmitt from a private field, flying close to the water and hedge-hopping some three metres above the trees across England. He enjoyed this immensely, since such close flying was prohibited in Germany. When he arrived at his destination he climbed to 20,000 feet and baled out, since he was not sure he could safely land his plane. He maintains that Hitler did not know of his flight and that the entire manœuvre was designed to stop the war, because his knowledge of the English people convinced him that, unless some spectacular step was taken, the English would continue to fight Germany until one country or the other was totally destroyed. He realised this after the fall of Poland and he believed that only he could get the English King or his representatives to meet with Hitler and make peace so that millions of people and thousands of villages would be spared. He knew Hitler would not permit him to do this so he took it upon himself.

"Hess recalls his stay in England fairly completely, and remembers clearly his first suicidal attempt. He was very depressed at the time, and planned to kill himself because he felt that he had failed in his mission and also because he felt at times that he was going insane. He recalled his head-first dive (*vide* p. 48, Ed.) into the stairway from the second storey and states that he jumped with such force that he turned over once in the air and struck the railing at the foot of the stairs, landing on his leg, which was broken. His attitude during this interview was co-operative, but he maintained an aloofness which has been characteristic of him since his arrival in prison. He

refused to take any type of medicine, and when it was pointed
out that his weight was definitely under normal, he stated that
there was no need to gain weight at the trial since at its conclusion he would be free to live at home with his family. There
in pleasant surroundings he would undoubtedly regain his
weight. Of course, if they executed him, it made little difference
whether he was fat or thin. Consequently he would not take
vitamins or any other medication.

"In this interview he was more friendly than at any time
before or since. He was deeply appreciative of any comment
upon his skill as an actor and in general was extremely happy
that he had been so successful.

"The reaction of his fellow prisoners was not so enthusiastic.
Goering was amazed and upset, and while he enjoyed the
frustration of the Court, demonstrated considerable resentment
that he had been so completely fooled. Von Schirach felt that
such behaviour was not the action of a normal man, and while
he enjoyed Hess's jest upon the world, felt that it was not a
gesture expected of a good German whose position was as
important as that of Hess. Ribbentrop, upon learning the
news, was dumbfounded, and was hardly able to speak when
told Hess's statement, and merely kept repeating: 'Hess, you
mean Hess? The Hess we have here? He said that?' Ribbentrop became quite agitated and seemed to feel such action was
not possible. He stated: 'But Hess did not know me. I looked
at him. I talked to him. Obviously he did not know me. It is
just not possible. Nobody could fool me like that.'

"Streicher's comment, as usual, was direct and blunt: 'If
you ask me, I think Hess's behaviour was a shame. It reflects
on the dignity of the German people.'

"The next day, Hess was in good spirits, and was interviewed
concerning his delusional beliefs. These are apparently still
with him, and he seems somewhat concerned about them. He
mentioned these ideas to Schirach, whom he cautioned about
eating his biscuits. It seems that Schirach was unusually
hungry, and had requested Hess to give him one of the biscuits,
which Hess frequently set aside and refused to touch. Hess
warned Schirach, stating that his biscuits were frequently
specially treated, and that if Schirach tasted them he would be
harmed. Hess was extremely mysterious about this and told

Schirach that some day he would explain the real reason for this cautioning.

"Although Hess was quite co-operative following his memory recall, he showed very little interest in any discussion dealing with Hitler or the effect of the Nazi Party on Germany. When asked about the statements Hitler had made to the Press concerning Hess's insanity at the time of his flight to England, he angrily replied: 'I do not know what he said. I do not want to know. He does not interest me.' He undoubtedly felt quite bothered about this rejection by Hitler, but on further discussion stated that under the circumstances such an attitude was logical.

"During the next two weeks, Hess became somewhat more amenable to discussion, but always maintained an arrogant front, standing at attention during an interview, refusing to shake hands, and not adopting the friendly reactions which were common in other prisoners in the jail. He was also suspicious of everyone and would frequently refuse to discuss his history or feelings.

"Hess's suspiciousness has been manifested during his entire stay in the prison by countless little actions. One of the most interesting of these was his refusal to sign his name to anything. This became ludicrously apparent during his examination by the French psychiatrist, Dr. Jean Delay, who requested his signature as an example of his handwriting. Hess would write the signature and immediately scratch it out. This occurred several times. I asked him to write, in accordance with my practice, a brief autobiographical study. Although this request was granted by every other prisoner in the jail, Hess refused on the grounds that it might be published to his detriment. I then asked him for a sample of his handwriting for graphological analysis. This idea impressed him and he stated that graphology was an extremely important science. He agreed to my request therefore and wrote a very innocuous description of his cell.

"Occasionally, a guard would request autographs in order to form a personal collection. On one occasion, one soldier had secured several autographs on a dollar bill. He handed it to Hess with the request to sign. Hess asked what it was for. The soldier explained. Hess smiled, agreed to sign, took the bill and went to the back of his cell. He then faced the soldier, smiled again, bowed, and proceeded to tear the bill into little fragments which he threw out of the window. Hess smiled again to the soldier and said: 'Our German signatures are precious.'

"On the 15th of December, in an interview, he stated that he could now follow the trial much better, but he admitted: 'It was not so clear at first after my memory came back, but it is clear now.' By this time he had apparently given up his desire to maintain his original version of faking all the time. He seemed to accept the viewpoint that it was not all simulation but he shied violently away from any suggestion of a mental disturbance. He felt deeply about his English flight and stated: 'I have the satisfaction of knowing that I tried to do something to end the war.'

"Conversation with Hess was difficult because he contributed very little to a discussion, limiting himself only to direct answers to questions. For this reason intelligence tests were difficult to administer. A test given on the 5th of November, before his memory was admitted, indicated a good average intelligence with some memory deficit. The impressions of Dr. Gustave Gilbert, the psychologist who administered the test, was that 'all intellectual functions were intact with a somewhat defective memory. The manner of performance suggests an auto-suggested hysterical element rather than a psychosis'. Readministration of the tests after November 30th indicated some slight improvement in the memory level but the over-all performance was essentially the same and we may conclude that Hess's intelligence falls in the high average class, but that he is not superior.

"Undoubtedly one of the reasons for his spectacular Court performance was the result of a discussion with the psychologist just before his dramatic recovery. His lawyer had apparently told him that the Court might declare him insane and if so he would not stand trial. This idea was emphasised by the psychologist just before Hess entered the court-room and this suggestion undoubtedly upset him considerably, since he felt that to be denied a trial would indicate mental inferiority and he felt that he must stand trial with his companions. This sort of reaction again emphasises his hysterical nature and his desire to thrust himself into the limelight, fatal as it might be, instead of attempting to escape by continued pretence.

"During the month of December, Hess became increasingly preoccupied with his food, and several times told us that he felt that the food was tampered with. On one occasion, during an interview, he became quite confidential, sat down on his cot, and asked if I, as a psychiatrist, could explain to him why he had these suspicions. He wanted to know if an individual with a strong mind could possibly entertain such ideas, or did they indicate a process of insanity. I asked him what ideas he had in mind, and he described at length the suspicions he had entertained in England that he was being poisoned. He admitted that such ideas were peculiar, but stated that he could not control them. He then added: 'Even now, at times these ideas come over me. I will look at a piece of bread or a bit of food and suddenly I feel sure that it has been poisoned. I try to talk myself out of this belief, but usually solve the problem by simply putting the food away. Occasionally, however, I force myself to eat it and then invariably have an attack of stomach cramps or feelings of giddiness which merely confirms my idea.' That these ideas were real was obvious to his jailers, since it became a matter of necessity to search his cell each day, and on each search numerous bits of food, carefully wrapped, would be found secreted in various parts of his cell.

"At one time the problem became too much for him, and during a discussion with Dr. Gilbert he stated: 'There is something I would like you to do. Yesterday I got a headache from eating crackers.' Here he pulled out a cellophane-wrapped bag of biscuits and offered one to the doctor, saying: 'Would you be good enough to eat these and see if they give you a headache? And this too.' He then picked up another box of cellophane-wrapped crackers, giving one of each to the doctor. The doctor ate the crackers. Hess said: 'Of course it might be just accidental on account of my continuous stomach cramps. I would not have given it any thought, but it has happened twice now.' The next day, when the doctor reported that the crackers did not give him a headache or any ill effect, Hess dismissed the subject with: 'Well, I guess it was not the crackers. Maybe it was some other type of food.'

"Goering reported about this time that Hess had approached him in the court-yard and asked him if he had noticed the noise of the machinery under their cell. Goering said certainly he noticed the noise which was made by the electric generators, and asked him what about it. Hess replied that undoubtedly these motors had been specially installed simply to keep them awake at night, to get their nerves on edge so that they would perhaps break during the trial. Goering laughed the whole thing off and told Hess that that was obvious nonsense, but reported his suspicions, maintaining that Hess definitely was not mentally sound. This seems to be the general conclusion of all of Hess's companions. Goering in particular felt that Hess had never been quite right, and stated this was the main reason why he was opposed when Hess was nominated as the No. 3 man in the Reich. At this time Goering and Hess were both on the platform, and Hitler was making the address announcing the movement of the German Armies into Poland. He named Goering as his successor, and then added that if anything happened to Goering, Hess would take over. This announcement upset Goering tremendously. After the speech he rushed up to Hitler demanding to know why such a weak, inferior personality could be named as his (Goering's) successor. Hitler quieted him down, and then pointed out that Hess was an old Party member, and had worked hard for them and should be rewarded. Hitler emphasised that such public recognition was reward enough for Hess, and that after all, should Goering become Chancellor of the Reich, he could then throw Hess out and appoint any successor he wanted. Goering felt very definitely that Hess was an inadequate personality, always suspicious, and unable to do things for himself.

"Von Schirach emphasised this inadequacy, stating that Hess was always shy and quiet, but believed that Hess, like himself, was one of the few Nazis who genuinely believed in the good of the Party. He stated that Hess was particularly attracted by the uniforms, the bands and the gala programmes. He also pointed out that Hess was always second to somebody in the Reich. His whole function at important meetings was to introduce the Fuehrer. He attempted to compete with Goering in aviation but always came off second best. Von Schirach felt that this constant defeat had preyed upon Hess's mind and believed that it was this that made him decide to fly to England. As Schirach puts it: 'With one act he could then become the most important man in the world, replacing Goering and almost eclipsing the Fuehrer.'

"Bohle, who knew Hess well, agreed with such a conception. He stated that Hess was forced to limit his speeches to congratulatory talks with women who had given birth to large numbers of children. Hess seemed to like to do this sort of thing, but before each speech, minor though it was, actually 'sweated blood' getting it written. Bohle also pointed to the 'boy scout' attitude of Hess; his failure to realise any of the wrong-doings of Hitler and his complete adoration of the man. He felt that Hess was extremely sincere, and only woke up to what Hitler was doing after the Polish war, with the concomitant massacre of the Polish citizens. He felt that Hess's flight to England was the result of the desire to escape from such cruelty as well as the need to demonstrate his value to the German people. Bohle stressed the fact that Hitler did not know about Hess's flight, and admits that he was the one who translated a letter for Hess to carry to the Duke of Hamilton.

"Goering and Ribbentrop both agree with Bohle on this point, and descriptions of Hitler's behaviour when he heard of Hess's flight offer convincing evidence that Hitler knew nothing about it until he received the letter which Hess had written to him.

"During the rest of my acquaintance with Rudolf Hess he continued courteous but aloof. His paranoid ideas continued but did not increase in scope or severity. His hysterical symptoms remained unchanged. He was the only prisoner with whom rapport was not developed and, while co-operative, was always formal, and maintained the attitude that he was a very important member of a still important Party. He flatly refused to the very end to admit the total defeat of the Nazi Party or to give up the idea that he was not an outstanding German patriot. This attitude carried on, and on my departure he was the only prisoner who failed to thank me for my interest in his welfare. This is typical of Hess's personality—a paranoid and suspicious individual with gross hysterical manifestations who failed in the most spectacular effort of his life—just as he has always failed. He considers himself to be the only standard-bearer left of the Nazi Party, and will continue true to his adolescent ideals to the end—provided of course that his basic instability does not precipitate another psychotic episode."

CHAPTER XIV

RUDOLF HESS—BEHAVIOUR RECORD AFTER NUREMBERG "RECOVERY"

G. M. Gilbert, Ph.D.
Prison Psychologist, International Military Tribunal

HESS was quite pleased with the sensation he had created in court and in the Press by having "fooled everybody", and for a time kept up the pretence of having completely simulated his amnesia. He told the writer immediately after his recovery that he could have done better on the psychological tests too, if he had tried, implying that that was part of his game. Re-test on the Wechsler-Bellevue Intelligence Test showed no significant improvement, however, except in digit-span (a test of immediate rote-memory or concentration-span), which jumped from a previous maximum of five digits repeated correctly to a new maximum of eight digits repeated correctly. The fluctuation of digit-span proved to be a faithful indicator of his memory and cognitive ability throughout the trial, corroborating the more elaborate memory tests. (See memory chart). Neither the Thematic Apperception Test nor the Rorschach showed any improvement in the limited cognitive and creative-ideational capacities upon re-test. As far as the tests were concerned, therefore, there was no question of malingering.

It became almost immediately clear why Hess had resorted to the pretext of malingering upon announcing his "recovery"; his mental state was an extremely delicate subject, especially with respect to his prestige among the Party leaders. (His secretary, Fräulein Fath, had already described how Hitler had chided him for his superstitions and peculiarities, and Goering had told us how Hess had generally been thought "queer" by most of the Party leaders.)

Two days after his dramatic "recovery" I broached the subject of Hitler's attitude towards his mental state and flight to England, merely asking him if he knew what Hitler had said and done about it at the time.

Hess bristled and retorted: "I don't know what he said and I don't want to know! It doesn't interest me!" But caught off guard upon further questioning, he revealed that he did know that Hitler had called him insane and ordered his name to be removed from public places.

His sudden temporary recovery seems to have been precipitated by the threat of being removed from the Court as incompetent, though Hess pretended at first that this merely made him decide to stop the "pretence". Hess did not keep up the pretence of a pretence very long, however. Two weeks later he was already referring to it as the "return of memory" and the "clearing-up" of his thinking and concentration ability. The cognitive processes had, in fact, cleared up. More than at any time before or since, he was able to discuss politics with clarity and understanding, though not without prejudice and a certain passive suggestibility that was always present when his suspicious, negativistic defences broke down. On this occasion (December 16th) he went so far as to admit that the Nazi "ideal" of breaking down class distinctions had merely substituted a vicious system of racial discrimination which was far worse, and that the Nazi racial ideology was probably a mistake. At this point his "concentration ability" (our mutually understood term for his mental state) was at its peak, and the digit-span test reached an all-time high—eight forward, seven backward. This was also the only time at which he did not complain of mental fatigue. Insight, orientation, and even affect appeared to be normal. In conversations he fully abandoned the pretence of having "simulated" his amnesia, but would only say that he had exaggerated it somewhat. Both the fellow-defendants and his defence counsel, Dr. Rohrscheidt, were amazed at the completeness and detailed clarity of his memory for all past events, and received complete co-operation in the preparation of the defence.

About four to six weeks after his "recovery", he started to complain of mental fatiguability again, and the first signs of secretiveness and negativism with vaguely paranoid ideas began to appear. He began talking about some mystic revelation he was going to make at the trial, until it became rather a joke among the defendants. However, his memory and reasoning ability still appeared normal, and the pretence of simulation had been completely abandoned.

The following diary excerpts reveal his mental state during this period.

December 26th. (conversation in Hess's cell).

(He is asked whether his memory had begun to clear up before the special Court session in which he announced his "recovery".)

"No, that all happened rather quickly just before the beginning of the special session on my case."

"Then it was more the effect of my telling you that you might be considered incompetent just before the session."

"Yes, that is undoubtedly it. . . . By the way, there is something—maybe it is still an *idée fixe*—but I got a headache from eating crackers again yesterday." Here he pulled out a little cellophane wrapping of ten-in-one ration crackers, and offered me one. "Would you be good enough to eat this and tell me if it gives you a headache?—And this too." He then picked up a K ration package of crackers and handed me one. I started to eat the two crackers, and he began to feel a little foolish. "Of course, it may be just accidental on account of my continuous stomach cramps. I wouldn't have given it any thought, but it happened twice."

"Are you getting along all right on your defence?" I asked, munching the crackers. "Can you concentrate all right?"

"Yes, but I still get tired after a while. I cannot concentrate steadily; I have to rest once in a while, either lie down or stop working for a minute. That is why I have to conserve my energy during this recess to work on my defence."

"Well, I'll let you know if the crackers give me a headache or any ill effects . . ."

(The next day I told him there were no ill effects, and he dismissed the idea.)

January 5th, 1946 (from conversation in Schacht's cell).

Schacht: " . . . By the way, Hess is crazy. He's concocting some kind of a mystic notion about the whole thing. I mentioned that I could even understand killing under certain circumstances, but stealing and graft requires a basically vile character. You know what I told you about Goering. I also told him that I had supported the Fuehrer until 1938 and then realised that he was a criminal; that I even made my first attempt to get rid of him after the Witzleben affair—that is how we got talking about the whole thing. Then suddenly he says to me mysteriously: 'Yes I can explain all that.' Mind you, he had never heard of these things before; he suddenly says: 'Yes, I can explain all these things—Goering's enrichment, the Witzleben affair, everything—just wait and see!' Can you imagine that? Wow! What a spectacle that is going to be when he gets up to give that final speech!"

January 6th, 1946 (from a conversation in Hess's cell).

He was in a comparatively communicative mood, and we discussed his flight to England. He denied having flown there to see the King or to bring him to Germany. He said he merely wanted to see the Duke of Hamilton, who, he assumed, would communicate his proposals to the King. He admitted the suicide attempt and the suspicions of being poisoned. "It must have been an *idée fixe*, but it is really remarkable how an idea could be so fixed that even now it sometimes occurs to me, maybe it was true after all. But of course, reason tells me that it couldn't be so."

I asked him about his "concentration" during the confinement in England, and how he reacted to the turn the war was taking. He thereupon spoke quite freely about his memory loss. "The first period of memory loss was really genuine—I suppose it must have been the continual isolation, and the disillusionment also played a role—but in the second period I exaggerated somewhat. It wasn't entirely loss of memory." He gave no indication of how these "periods" corresponded to the clinical data, and I had to avoid the appearance of examining him, in order to maintain rapport.

I asked him about his amnesia in Nuremberg.

"Well, if I hadn't actually had a period of real loss of memory before," Hess said, "I wouldn't have been able to exaggerate it so well. I wouldn't have known how to do it; there would have been no reference point."

"I understand. One can sort of suggest himself into it until it is a real memory loss that required practically no voluntary effort."

"Yes, that is it," Hess agreed with the positiveness that distinguished insight from response to suggestion. "Sometimes one doesn't know whether it is exaggeration or not. One simply does not remember, that is all."

" . . . And then too," I suggested, "this solitary confinement was hardly conducive to mental stimulation."

"That is true too. I suppose the contact with the others up in the Court and on our walks was beginning to stimulate me after the trial started."

"Had you begun to recognise Goering and the others around you even before that special session?"

"Yes, a little, but everything really cleared up at once that afternoon in Court after you spoke to me. But I still get tired from thinking too much. Even now for instance, the test and even just the conversation gradually tire me out, so I have to lie down." I told him he could lie down, and terminated the interview with the assurance that he could call on me for any help he needed.

February 9th. 1946 (from conversation in Speer's cell).

. . . Finally he reported that Hess was using him for a "physiological experiment". Hess had given him a little package of sugar and asked him to use it in his coffee and notice whether it did not produce diarrhoea. "When Hess asked me about it the next day," Speer related, "I thought I would try a psychological experiment myself, and I told him that I did not get diarrhoea, but if I was not mistaken, I was becoming constipated instead. So Hess says: 'Yes, yes; I think in certain quantities it can have the opposite effect,' and he asked me to report how my bowel movements went; what a screwball!"

AMNESIA RELAPSE

In the meantime his memory began to deteriorate, and a relapse of the original amnesia began to set in. At the end of January, or seven weeks after his "recovery", memory defect already became noticeable, as the following diary excerpts show:

January 20th, 1946 (from examination in Hess's cell).

Re-test on TAT (Thematic Apperception Test) shows same extreme cognitive and affective constriction as during amnesia period. In addition, his failure to remember ever having seen any of the cards shown to-day (6-10), as well as a sharp decrease in digit span, indicate a probable relapse of memory and

G

concentration. This is supported by his introspective observation that his "ability to concentrate" has deteriorated in
the last few days. It was noted in casual conversation that
serious gaps were present in his recollections of the recent events
at the trial. . . .

Towards the end of to-day's session, I told him that I had
shown him these cards before. He seemed quite shocked, and
fell back on the cot in surprise, supporting himself on his
elbows.

"You don't say!—Did you really?" he whispered. I hastened
to assure him that I did not expect him to remember them,
since I originally showed them during his amnesia period, and
these little incidents would not necessarily return to his memory
as readily as the events of his life history. He accepted this
explanation eagerly, and commented: "Actually to-day is a
particularly bad day—I can hardly concentrate at all, and I
am not even working on my defence. I hope it goes away."

"It is understandable that the fatigue of these weeks of trial
will impair your concentration. I suppose the frustration of
your ideals by the damaging evidence of what took place in
your absence also puts a strain on you."

"Yes, that is probably so," he agreed. "I cannot understand
how I could have done such things."

"So you needn't worry about temporary impairment of
concentration. But you mustn't exaggerate it either of your
own free will."

"No, I certainly do not want to do that. If I did this time
nobody would believe me after I had said I had deliberately
faked my amnesia. I hope it doesn't stay this way." He then
retreated to his characteristic guarded, withdrawn attitude
though apparently accepting my assurance that I would help
him by continuing our interviews and exercises.

January 27th, 1946 (from examination in Hess's cell).

Still apathetic, withdrawn, and somewhat secretive. As for
the trial, he wasn't listening very attentively, he said, because
the French talk so much and so much of it is repetition. He
admitted that he didn't remember all of what had gone before,
but the others had told him that most of it was repetition.
He still could not understand what had brought the atrocities
about. He has hardly been in communication with his family,

but expresses no great interest in them, very much unlike the rest of the defendants. Has also lost interest in seeing his secretaries again.

From his attitude, I gathered that the current apathy and beginnings of real and ostensible memory failure were part of the negativistic pattern of reaction to the final smashing of the ideology which had supported his ego and now faced him with an intolerable choice between accepting a share of the guilt of Nazism or rejecting his Fuehrer. He will probably end by hysterically rejecting reality again, and converting it into some unpredictable functional disturbance, either amnesia or paranoia, or a mixture of these and other symptoms.

The prediction was not long in being realised. His memory decreased rapidly from week to week, blocking out more and more recent events. Finally he could not even remember events of the day before. He soon forgot the circumstances of his flight and imprisonment in England, except in so far as constant reminders at the trial kept a verbal identification of the event alive for a time. The results of various examinations during the six month period following his "recovery" are summarised in the table below. The main events of his life and main witnesses in the trial are used as reference points to indicate the progressive amnesia: (see next page).

The relapse was likewise confirmed by indirect means. As the time for Hess's defence approached, there was consternation in the prisoners' dock as they realised that Hess was in fact losing his memory. They had been taking it for granted that he had been malingering in the beginning after his apparently complete recovery. But those for whom Hess was supposed to give supporting testimony, as former Deputy Party Leader, were greatly disconcerted to find that Hess no longer remembered what they were talking about when they reminded him of the questions he was supposed to answer for them.

March 10th, 1946 (from conversation in von Schirach's cell).

. . . Suddenly von Schirach asked me: "By the way, what is the matter with Hess? About two weeks ago I discussed two questions which he was supposed to answer for me on the witness stand. The next day he told me he had the answers, knew all about it, and even remembered the date in question. So the day before yesterday I asked him about those questions again, and he didn't even know what I was talking about. I looked at him and said: 'But Herr Hess, we discussed it only eight days ago and you even remembered the date!' 'I am terribly sorry,' he said, 'but I simply cannot remember. Try as I may, I simply cannot keep my memory intact.' Now, what do you think of that?"

Hess's Memory Chart since "Recovery"

Date of Examination

Event	Dec. 1	Dec. 16	Jan. 20	Feb. 24	Mar. 2	Mar. 17	Apr. 6	May 11	Ju. 2
Childhood Events	3	3		o					
Nazi Party	3	3	2	1	1	½	o	o	
Flight to England	3	3	2	1	1	1	1	½	o
Trial: (a) Psychiatric Examination	3	2	1	o	o	o	o	o	o
(b) Witness General Lahousen (Dec. 1)		3	1	o	o	o	o	o	o
(c) Witness von dem Bach-Szilewski (Jan. 7)			2	o	o	o	o	o	o
(d) Witness General von Paulus (Feb. 12)				3	1	o	o	o	o
(e) Goering's Defence (March 8–22)						1	o	o	o
(f) Hess's own Defence (March 25–26)							o	o	o
Approximate Recollection Span (limit for incomplete recollection)	life	life	2 mos.	2 wks.	2 wks.	2 days	1 day	1 day	½ day
Digit Span Test (Total forward and backward	12	15	9		7	7		8	7

3 = normal recollection (allowing for normal forgetting)
2 = incomplete recollection, absence of essential details.
1 = slight recollection, barely identifying event.
o = no recollection whatever.

March 14th, 1946 (from conversation in Goering's cell).

" . . . As far as Hess is concerned, I must admit you have me licked. His memory is definitely shot, and I don't believe any more that he was faking in the first place. He even admitted a couple of weeks ago that he really had suffered amnesia in England, and said it wasn't all fake here either—just as you always said. On that score I am thoroughly convinced. God, what a farce it is going to be when he gets up to testify!"

The dynamics of the relapse seem to involve a basically hysterical-schizoid personality resorting to the same ego-protecting mechanism that brought about the withdrawal from reality in England and the "recovery" in Nuremberg. The sources of Hess's increasing frustration at the trial were two-fold: For one, there was the constant accumulation of evidence of the sins of the Nazi regime with the murderous cruelty of the Fuehrer. To this, Hess could only keep repeating: "I don't understand: I don't understand," and seemed to be searching for ways of rejecting or rationalising the grim reality. The second was the presentation of the case against him in Court, which made his flight to England look ridiculous even to his own comrades, as the following diary excerpt shows:

February 7th, 1946 (from court-room observation).

In the afternoon, Mr. Griffith-Jones presented the case against Hess. The prosecutor's scorn was shared by even the defendants, who felt partly amused and partly disgraced by the naïve and presumptuous gesture by Hess in offering the British peace on his terms. During the presentation, Goering repeatedly turned to Hess and asked him if he had really said that. Hess nodded that he had. At the end of the session, Goering, hardly able to control his own scorn at Hess's attempt to meddle in diplomacy, slapped him on the back in mock congratulation and encouragement for a good try. After they had gone down in the elevator, the others expressed themselves. Von Papen, von Neurath, Fritzsche, Schacht and Funk literally threw up their hands in expressions of disgust and desperation at "such stupidity . . . such childish naïveté . . . that was what Hitler called a political leader." All except Schacht believed that Hitler had not sent him on that mission, and that it was an irresponsible dramatic gesture. Fritzsche mentioned that the flying ace, Udet, had testified at the time that an ME110 couldn't land in Britain under those conditions, and that Hess had probably landed in the Channel.

"Yes," commented Funk wryly, "all the insane, drunk, and childish are protected by God." He did not specify under which heading he classified Hess. "But seriously, it is not funny—it is disgraceful, it shows what irresponsible people ruled Germany. There is a point at which things stop being funny and become disgraceful."

. . . Von Pápen reiterated his opinion of the stupidity of Hess's mission to England, and ridiculed his childish attempt at diplomacy. Like Goering, he said that he himself could have contacted the British at a moment's notice through a neutral power, if there was any real negotiating to do. In general, his attitude was that fools rush in where angels fear to tread, and that, by further implication, included that fool Ribbentrop.

The very next day I noticed that Hess was reading a book in the dock and not paying any attention to the opening of the Russian prosecutor's case. At lunch I asked him why. Hess said that he didn't have to listen to foreigners slandering his country. (It was a significant repetition of his statement with regard to his amnesia on the second day of the trial.) I pointed out that even if he disagreed, it was necessary to hear what they had to say, in order to prepare his own defence. "That is a matter that concerns only me," he retorted.

This protective negativism increased from that time on. As he withdrew from contact with the frustrating environment, he became more and more preoccupied with his own mystic and paranoid thoughts, maintaining a secretive attitude about his "big revelation" even towards the other defendants. Several of them told me that he was the only one who never discussed his case with them. Soon they began to be amused by Hess's queerness. Goering was overheard in the dock passing jibes at Hess's "principles" and making a motion that Hess let them in on his "big secret". Upon examination Hess made no reference to his big secret, but would occasionally complain about the noise the guards were making deliberately to interfere with his mental state. He thought that somebody "higher up" was plotting to interfere with his defence by having the guards disturb his concentration ability, but he wasn't sure. His suspicion of the food continued, but manifested itself overtly only in little signs of cautiousness over what he accepted.

Dr. Seidl, Hess's defence counsel, asked me to tell the prosecution that there would be no sense in cross-examining Hess, because his memory was very bad, and it would serve no purpose. (However, he had got sufficient information from Hess's period of recovery to make an adequate defence.)

The day before he was supposed to take the stand (March 24th) Hess told me he had changed his mind about it. (He had fully intended to take the stand on his own and fellow defendants' behalf. He had even written down the answers to the questions he was going to be asked to make sure he could answer them, but had grown apprehensive of betraying his limitations upon cross-examination.) His defence counsel presented his defence without putting Hess on the stand, giving the excuse that his client "did not recognise the Court". He admitted to me privately, however, that Hess's loss of memory was the real reason. Two days later Hess had forgotten that two witnesses had been presented in his defence (he could barely recall one) and ten days later he had forgotten that he had made any defence at all.

As the amnesia became more and more complete, there was less and less evidence of any paranoid trend. Hess was apparently forgetting what his delusions and suspicions were. However, the suspicion of his food continued in an absent-minded sort of way. Significantly, at an early stage of the relapse, he resorted to a device to remind himself of his suspicions: he wrote on the cardboard top of his cell table: "Do not take sleeping pills. . . . Instead of eggs; ask for marmalade and bread. Keep an empty stomach in the morning."

As the defence of the Nazi war criminals nears its conclusion (June, 1946), Hess has completely reverted to the withdrawn, apathetic state with total amnesia in which he came to Nuremberg.

Test Summary.

A battery of three psychological tests was administered to Rudolf Hess during his amnesic period in Nuremberg before the trial started (November, 1945) and again during his period of recovery (December-January). The tests were: *Wechsler-Bellevue* (Adult Intelligence Test), *Rorschach* (psychodiagnostic Ink-blot Test), and Thematic Apperception Test (story-telling from pictures).

The clinical picture was essentially the same upon test and re-test; a neurotic-schizoid personality with slightly above average intelligence, severely constricted in affect and creative-ideational capacity. The individual test results were as follows:

Wechsler-Bellevue Intelligence Test: The general performance was slightly above average, but the scatter of scores on the sub-tests was characteristic of the neurotic. Sensori-motor co-ordination and power of observation were about average-adult; comprehension and reasoning were above average-adult level. The span of apprehension as measured by the digit-span test fluctuated with his amnesic state, being below average during amnesia (five forward, four backward), above average during recovery (eight forward, seven backward), and far below average again upon relapse (four forward, three backward). The test of general information was above average, but showed some selective blocking during the amnesic period. The manner of response and performance during the original test showed a large element of ostentatious auto-suggestive "helplessness" characteristic of the hysteric, although rapport was good. The performance was better upon re-test, but the improvement could be largely attributed to the practice effect, except for digit-span. The repetition of many of the same failures ruled out his pretence of malingering on the original test. A reliable Intelligence Quotient cannot be given in this case, but would lie somewhere between 112 and 120.

Thematic Apperception Test. The TAT responses were meagre in the extreme, showing constriction of associative processes and creative thinking far beyond normal limits. In spite of a good deal of prodding, he was able to give only a meagre description of each picture, averaging about forty words, where the normal adult would spontaneously produce a story of 200-300 words on each picture. The material was entirely superficial and limited to the immediate situation represented by the stimuli. He proved to be incapable of projecting the situation into a continuity of past and future. When urged to try, he protested his lack of aptitude for fantasy and insisted: "I can't see any further than what is here." Because of the meagre-ness of production, only the slightest clues are given to the mechanism behind this rigid fixation on the immediate situation. In a few places, the situation suggests impotence, failure, escape into oblivion. Even in the realm of fantasy, Hess seemed to be forestalling frustration by not being able to think a given hypothetical situation through to its conclusion.

Rorschach. The meagre Rorschach record of fifteen responses is characterised by: the lifelessness of the figures seen, showing lack of (empathy) and inner life; the tendency to superficial structural-whole and built-up-whole figures, indicating a tendency to superficial generalisation in his outlook; the emotionally immature preoccupation with the animal and botanical world, and only lifeless details at that; emotional instability shown in the poor colour control, breaking out into the hysterical "blood" response in one place, which is signi-ficantly rationalised by a built-up-whole interpretation. The only places where a human figure and an animal figure are seen (both popular figures) they remain *drawn designs* rather than representations of living things. The only movement seen in the entire series is in a mechanical object. All of this bespeaks impotence and lack of vitality in his mental life; a lack of resilience and adaptability breaking out occasionally into uncontrolled emotional responses which is quickly rationalised. The environment consists essentially of figures without life, and there is no projection or contact in the dynamic sense.

Impression: The tests show erratic intellectual functioning slightly above average-adult level, but a severely constricted affect and lack of emotional contact characteristic of the schizoid personality.

CHAPTER XV

*In October, Dr. Gilbert recorded his last observations and with
these we can close the factual record.*

Third Recovery.

Hess remained in the same condition as described above
until the last day of the trial, August 31st. As the day for the
final speech approached, he displayed more and more anxiety
over the threat of betraying his mental handicap in public
before the other Nazi leaders. He remained in his cell, complaining of more intense and more continuous stomach cramps.
The demonstrative anxiety-resolving mechanism was obvious.
When asked by Dr. Dunn and myself why he didn't want to go
to Court to make his last stand with the others as No. 2 of the
Party, Hess retorted angrily: "What difference does it make
what number man I was in the Party? First of all it is a torture
to send me there in this condition, and second of all what good
is it if I stand there like a fool (blöd)?!" He complained bitterly
that his physical condition made it impossible for him to go to
Court, and if we were humane we would send him to the
hospital for the rest of the trial, for "diet control". Dr. Dunn
explained that there would be no point to that unless Hess was
willing to submit to medical treatment, but this Hess declined.

In the meantime, Dr. Seidl, Hess's attorney, submitted a
fourteen-page lay exposition on Hess's mental and physical
condition, requesting examination by another psychiatric
commission and a preliminary informative report from the
writer. The Tribunal requested the latter, and the following
report was submitted:

August 17th, 1946.

SUBJECT: Competence of Defendant Rudolf Hess.
TO: General Secretary, International Military Tribunal.

 1. In compliance with the Tribunal's request the following
facts and studied opinions are submitted with respect to the
competence of Rudolf Hess, based on my continual tests and

observations from October, 1945, to the present time, in the capacity of prison psychologist:

2. *Amnesia at beginning of trial.* There can be no doubt that Hess was in a state of virtually complete amnesia at the beginning of the trial. The opinions of the psychiatric commissions in this regard and with respect to his sanity have only been substantiated by prolonged subsequent observation.

3. *Recovery.* On the day of the special hearing in his case, November 30th, 1945, Rudolf Hess did, in fact, recover his memory. The cause of his sudden recovery is an academic question, but the following event probably played a part: Just before the hearing I told Hess (as a challenge) that he might be considered incompetent at that time and excluded from the proceedings, but I would sometimes see him in his cell. Hess seemed startled and said he thought he *was* competent. Then he gave his declaration of malingering in Court, apparently as a face-saving device. In later conversations he admitted to me that he had not been malingering, and that he knew he had lost his memory twice in England. During the months of December, 1945, and January, 1946, his memory was quite in order.

4. *Relapse.* At the end of January I began to notice the beginnings of memory failure. This increased progressively during February, until he returned to a state of virtually complete amnesia again about the beginning of March, and he has remained in that state ever since. (At the beginning of the relapse, Hess expressed anxiety over it, saying that no one would believe him this time after he had said he faked his amnesia the first time.) The amnesia is progressive, each day's events being quickly forgotten. At present his memory span is about half a day, and his apprehension span has dropped from eight to four (digits repeated correctly immediately after hearing).

5. *Competence and sanity.* I have read the application of Dr. Seidl both in German and in English, and wish to make the following comment:

(*a*) Lay discussion of psychiatric concepts does not help throw any light on this case, because psychiatrists themselves are not in agreement on the definition of terms like "psychopathic constitution", "hysterical reaction", etc., and these terms have entirely different meanings in English and German usage.

(*b*) The psychiatric commissions have agreed, and my further observations have confirmed, that Hess is *not* insane (in the legal sense of being incapable of distinguishing right from wrong or realising the consequences of his acts).

(*c*) Hess did recover his memory for a sufficient period of time (two to three months) to give his counsel ample co-operation in the preparation of his defence. If he failed to do so, it was the result of a negativistic personality peculiarity, which I have also observed, and not incompetence.

(*d*) There has been no indication in his case-history or present behaviour that he was insane at the time of the activities for which he has been indicted. His behaviour throughout the trial has also shown sufficient insight and reason to dispel any doubts about his sanity. (He may have gone through a psychotic episode in England, but that in no way destroys the validity of the previous two statements. He has exhibited signs of a "persecution complex" here too, but these have not been of psychotic proportions.)

(*e*) In my opinion, another examination by a psychiatric commission at this time would not throw any further light on the case, because the clinical picture is the same and the conclusions would necessarily be the same as those of the original psychiatric commissions, to wit: Hess is not insane but suffering from hysterical amnesia. I have discussed this case with the present prison psychiatrist, Lt.-Col. Dunn, who has recently examined Hess, and he is also of the opinion that Hess's present mental status is apparently the same as that indicated in the original psychiatric reports, which he has read.

G. M. Gilbert, Ph.D.
Prison Psychologist.

On the basis of this report the Tribunal decided not to order another psychiatric examination of Hess. But Hess was not finished springing his surprises. On the day of the final speeches, he suddenly changed his mind and appeared in Court. Just before the speeches started, he told Goering that he did not intend to make one. But when his turn came, he suddenly pulled some wrapped-up notes out of his pocket and made a speech giving his slightly paranoid explanation of the "mysterious influences" which explained Hitler's abnormal condition, the atrocities committed by the Germans and British, the Moscow and Nuremberg trials, his own treatment in captivity, etc., apparently the "big revelation" he had been threatening from the beginning. The notes served, no doubt, to maintain an unbroken thread of paranoid fixation throughout his period of amnesia, but it was apparent by the time he finished his speech that he had regained his memory. When I tested him in the intermission immediately following the speech and later at lunch and in his cell, it was obvious that his memory had been fully restored. He made a feeble attempt to pretend that he had been simulating amnesia again, but when I refused to accept it, he dropped the idea. The diary notes pick up the story from there:

August 31st (day of third recovery). . . . In his cell in the afternoon he was less inclined to pretend simulation. I told him: "See, I told you your memory would come back again just as it did the last time."

Hess nodded, but showed some concern over the impression he had made. "I suppose the Press will have the impression that I am entirely crazy," he said.

"Oh, perhaps, but I understand how it is—things are a little mixed up at the moment that your memory begins to come back."

Hess acquiesced, but was still grappling with the paranoid ideas. "But I can't get rid of the idea that things have been put into my food. Let me ask you (with a very forced laugh) would it be too much to ask you to take me out to the water tap to let me drink some water from it myself? There is one at the entrance to the jail."

I called in Lt.-Col. Dunn, and Hess repeated his request. He said, laughing again with a very forced laugh, that he just wanted a sign of good faith on our side to convince him that he was not getting specially treated water. We tried to humour him and asked the prison officer about it, but were told that the tap water was not fit to drink. When we communicated this to Hess, he laughed. "There, I told you so. I didn't expect anything different. Right now that only confirms my suspicions. I suppose by to-morrow they could fix it, but they won't let me drink it now." Col. Dunn explained that the tap water was not potable but everybody received chlorinated water for safety.

"You see?" he said to me. "Of course, that's the explanation you give. I didn't expect anything different."

Later Hess asked me what I had said in the report to which the Tribunal had referred. I said that I had stated that he had lost memory twice but was not insane. Hess accepted this.

September 1st. Hess showed a little more insight into his paranoid trend, and did not want to discuss it, realising that there was something unreal about it all. He was using the water poured out for him and made no further remarks about it.

He said he was thankful to the Court for interrupting him during his speech, because he suddenly realised that he was talking to a blank wall, and nobody would believe what he said no matter how long he talked. He had then simply confined himself to his concluding statement. I asked him whether this was the point at which things really suddenly became clear, and he said it was. Later, however, he tried to revert to the version of simulation, but was obviously using it half-heartedly as a face-saving device.

His memory for the events of the trial seemed to be quite complete. He recalled the various tests I had given him, could supply any desired details about his flight to England and events in general both remote and recent.

September 2nd. Hess has regained almost complete insight into the inappropriate nature of the paranoid trend that suddenly manifested itself during his recovery two days ago, and gave me a letter to give to Col. Andrus which he had written yesterday. He is apparently in the same state that he was in a few days after his last recovery, unable completely to abandon his suspicion of food, but not taking it very seriously.

Digit-span: eight forward, six backward.

September 4th. Hess is much calmer to-day, his stomach cramps having abated. Casual conversation and a letter he gave me to forward to his wife showed complete insight into his outburst in Court four days ago. There is no longer even the half-hearted pretence on his part that he had faked his amnesia again, and he is fully aware of the inappropriate nature of the paranoid outburst. He was even willing to discuss it a little. He explained that there was some reasonable basis for his suspicion of abnormal influences, because the French paper *Le Jour* had speculated that the Russian prisoners who confessed had been "doped up" at the famous Moscow trial; his friends in the dock had told him that Dr. Morel had given Hitler many injections, and he always thought that medication was harmful anyway; he could not help being suspicious of his own food in enemy captivity: he had noticed a strange expression in the eyes of some of the people who attended him, and the other Nazis had told him that Hitler had also developed a strange stare in recent years.

His reality-testing is good and he seems to realise that it was inappropriate to make too much of these speculations. He made it clear that he was trying to seek some kind of explanation for the incredible change in Hitler's "chivalrous" outlook towards solving the Jewish problem.

He remembers all the details of his flight to England, such as the two suicide attempts, his loss of memory, the doctors who attended him (Rees, Dicks, Jones, etc.) and is perfectly well oriented as to his role in the Nazi Party, the war, and the present trial.

September 12th. Hess very lucid and rather relaxed between attacks of stomach cramps, but entirely seclusive. He has refused to send for his wife, as the others have done, and has even declined to visit the other prisoners as permitted. His sensitivity over his mental state is apparently the decisive factor here. Freely admits second memory recovery in Nuremberg. Rapport enhanced by my testimonial that he is not insane.

October 1st (as the prisoners come down the jail, one by one, after hearing their sentences). Hess strutted in, laughing nervously, and said that he had not been listening, so he did not know what the sentence was, and what was more, he didn't care. As the guard unlocked his handcuffs, he asked why he had been handcuffed, and Goering had not. I said it was probably an oversight with the first prisoner. Hess laughed again and said mysteriously that he *knew* why, obviously alluding to his persecution complex. (A guard told me he had got a life sentence.)

In the days following the verdict, there was no essential change from the condition observed after both recoveries in Nuremberg: negativistic and seclusive, preoccupied with mild suspicions of persecution, but well oriented, with normal reasoning ability, insight, and memory.

From the *Evening Standard*, London, October 21st, 1946, "NUREMBERG, Monday—Hess is now displaying a keen alert memory, which he seems to enjoy showing off, Colonel Andrus said to-day."

CHAPTER XVI

GENERAL REVIEW OF THE CASE

IN assessing Hess's personality and its degree of morbidity in the direction of a paranoid psychosis, it will first be necessary to relate his behaviour to the cultural pattern which has formed his background. It is possible that much of his symptomatology, so extremely queer to a British milieu, might be found to differ not very greatly from the norm of Nazi and possibly even German modes of thinking and dealing with reality.

In this connection it is relevant to refer to a fairly thorough survey which was made by one of us (H. V. D.) in the years 1942-45 of the psychology of German prisoners of war with special emphasis on trying to analyse those traits of personality which were characteristic of men holding Nazi beliefs and convictions. The findings, which are briefly summarised in what follows, have been to a very large extent confirmed by other independent observers, notably Brickner,* H. G. Baynes†, and the Columbia University Conference on the future of Germany‡.

The Nazi movement would seem to have been but a late and, as it were, caricatured expression of modes of behaviour and aspiration which had been noted about the attitudes of the German élite long before the war of 1914-18. The outstanding among these were tendencies to exert power and domination, to have status and "honour", expansion hunger (Lebensraum) and a tendency to glorify mass movement as an expression of unity in subordination to a great leader figure.

In examining the personal histories of large numbers of prisoners of war and sorting these according to the degree of acceptance of Nazi nationalist and militarist aspirations, it was possible to find a correspondence between the fanaticism with which such views were held and the degree of acceptance of father rule in childhood. It is well known that, by and large,

* Brickner, Richard M. "Is Germany Incurable?" New York, 1943.
† Baynes, H. G. "Germany Possessed".
‡ Unpublished Memorandum; 1944.

German family culture is an authoritarian, patriarchal one, in
which the Prussian virtues of "manliness" and "hardness" have
been superimposed on the pliable emotional and passive
characteristics of the Germans. Perhaps the Prussian tradition
of discipline, ruthless force and domination were eagerly
accepted by the rest of Germany precisely because they were an
impressionable and "soft-skinned" people, to whom the cover of
virility was as acceptable as a shell to a snail. At any rate, the
tough Prussian brought unity and political order to Germany
and it became fashionable for the élite to assume this armour of
manliness and Herrenvolk display of strength which, for many
Germans, hides an inner conflict and lack of self-confidence.

It is characteristic of this manliness cult that it identifies
femininity with inferiority and instils a sense of guilt about any
qualities connected with or derived from the tender relations
between little boys and their mothers. The relegation of German women to relatively low status as child-bearers and house-
keepers is traditional. The typical description given by
German men of their childhood is of the father as complete
master in the home, whose decision mother would never
question. Men describe their fathers and themselves as having
the desire to mould their little sons in their own image and lick
them into shape. They express themselves as grateful, with a
queer sort of pride, for having been thrashed—a process which
they assert has made them into men. They invariably state that
they richly deserved beatings. In no case, except in one or two
highly cultivated and untypical Germans, was any criticism of
this paternal system expressed, whereas half-joking contempt
for maternal "sloppiness" and ineffectiveness was frequent.

The strong pre-eminence of the father in the typical German
home, coupled with the self-effacing submissive role of the
mother, results frequently in repression of tenderness needs and
in a markedly one-sided identification with paternal sternness
in the son. It makes the German child unduly dependent and
submissive to father figures. The paternal authority especially
issues psychologically in a severe conscience which exhorts to
such moral clichés as "iron duty", "self-mastery", "determination", "hard work", "industry and diligent self-improve-
ment". Several important results follow from this tenseness and
rigidity, which has been lifted into the group ideal and which is

not counteracted by the requisite degree of softening and counterweight from the maternal attitude, itself submissive and negative in the face of the domestic patriarch. The best known of the consequences of this situation is the submissiveness and subordination of the German national character. Owing to the necessity of being on good terms with the paternal authority, the sons superficially accept the situation and revaluate the father's sternness as part of his love for the son. The father principle is exalted into an ideal, after the pattern of which social institutions are moulded. This forcible submission, however, results in a sneaking sense of inferiority and weakness. One of the ways in which this shows itself in the German behaviour is in the prevalent need for status. In order to bolster up one's defective self-valuation, one builds society on the hierarchical principle in which everyone's place on the social ladder is rigidly determined. Rank, uniform and title are aspired to as methods of enhancing status and prestige and are used with serious formality beyond all rational need for distinguishing men's social function. Even in their "revolution" the Nazis, although out to form a new society, have re-created these complicated pyramids of ranks in all branches of their state, in order to satisfy status needs. This status anxiety leads to overvaluation, both of the individual by himself and of the national group. Germans as individuals and as members of their group, *vis-à-vis* foreigners, are very touchy so far as status—their so-called "honour"—is concerned. For the lack of dignity which Germans experience at the hands of their superiors they make up by assuming unnecessary degrees of hauteur and aggressiveness *vis-à-vis* their inferiors. Anyone who has resided in Germany could verify the tenseness and rank-consciousness of German society in which the inferiors accept their subordinate positions and in turn exact similar subordination from those still lower in the social scale. This same tendency has led to over-emphasis of the idea of group power and dignity especially in relation to weaker and therefore despised nations. This need to feel great and strong has been well exploited by German Nationalist propaganda. The German is stirred by the sense of might and order, of belonging to a mighty national organism about which he has created a legend of invincibility; it helps him personally to feel stronger. The greater the father figure to whom he can subordinate himself, the more manly and noble it is to submit to such a figure. One side of the German, therefore, is always bent on impressing the father figure, whether as his own conscience or as an external leader, with his goodness and efficiency and his complete compliance. Any rebel feeling among the broad mass of Germans one has examined is rare; few have run away from home or have defied their fathers or swung to views opposite to the parental mode of life. Most of them after a youthful fling come to heel and proceed to re-create in themselves the stern, sober father figure, taking pleasure in petty tyranny and severe authority over others and kow-towing to those above them.

An important result of this situation is the strong ambivalence from which many Germans can be seen to suffer and which can, without serious fear of contradiction, be reduced to the dilemma of dealing with the father authority, which is loved and hated at the same time. Whilst the outwardly zealous submission to this authority is made more palatable by unconscious identification with the father, there remains a residue of hatred which is responsible for many of the more unpleasant manifestations of German group behaviour, and which comes out—even in individual contacts—in a much greater tenseness, touchiness and humourlessness of Germans than, say, of Anglo-Saxons. One way in which the German appears typically to deal with this hate residue is in a tendency to what has been well named "the romantic revolt". In this aspect, which is much more unconscious, he feels himself identified with a hero who rescues primarily his mother, and so his homeland, or his German soul from the tyrannical oppressor. This tendency has resulted in the many movements of pseudo-emancipation in the cultural history of Germany, usually coloured by an extravagant "return to nature" or to the primitive, to sexual licence and the like. Its better manifestations resulted in the creation of the wonderful treasure-house of German romantic literature, poetry and music. At its worst it has been a dangerous introspection and search for the depths, sanctified as a quest for the hidden springs of power of the German soul. Nazism especially exploited some of these tendencies and systematised a mechanism which was never far below the surface of the German character into a political code of behaviour. This is the mechanism of projection. Germans seem to have great difficulty in accepting in themselves considerable charges of smouldering hatred against the paternal authority. Therefore, at a time when economic and social conditions had produced a general feeling of dissatisfaction with authorities—now felt to be bad—a revolution was averted by the widest possible use of projection mechanisms; guilt tension was relieved by being directed on to outside scapegoats who were regarded as the only disturbers of the peace. Aggressive rebellious forces could be attributed to the agency of wicked outsiders, and the belief that all within the fold were good sons was thereby restored. Two such scapegoat symbols were ready to hand—the Jews and the Bolsheviks. The success of these scapegoats can only be attributed to the average German's intolerance of his own aggressive tendencies. The average German is extremely touchy and squeamish about brutality and goes to great trouble to provide alibis and to repudiate evidence of sadism in his group. This side of the German has been very clearly illustrated at the Nuremberg trials in the elaborate attempts at whitewashing their conduct. The notion of being surrounded by envious rich powers who wanted to keep Germany impotent, or destroy her at the behest of the Jewish-Bolshevik conspiracy, became one of the great theme-songs of Nazi propaganda, and was found to be widely and fanatically believed by something like thirty per cent of Hitler's soldiers down to 1944. The individual German has felt so small and helpless in his personal relations with his father that he has tended to project this situation into his national destiny. He has been eager and gratified to find any elements of reality which have corresponded to this fantasy. For that reason the Nazis have harped so much on the injustice of the Treaty of Versailles or on any signs of Soviet militarisation. It is of course also true that paranoid behaviour at last results in defensive measures on the part of the neighbours and so to some extent provides later real confirmation of the initially persecutory fears.

It is a curious thing, however, that despite all that has been said about German notions of being a master race, uniquely great and misunderstood because of a Messianic promise to bring order to a disunited world, they have at the same time retained some degree of insight into their weakness. Many

Nazis, as well as others, have confided to us that their national character was weak and divided and have expressed admiration for the greater unity, *savoir-faire* and capacity for rulership of the English. Envious admiration of their rich and successful British cousins has been a very constant theme in these men's conversation with us. They have been borne out in the behaviour of Kaiser Wilhelm II's regime and later on in the slavish imitation of English mannerisms, clothes, uniforms and many other points. It can be accepted from intelligence records now revealed that this ambivalence towards England affected even Hitler himself, and appears to have introduced a curious indecision into all his plans for dealing militarily with the recalcitrant British in 1940-41.

It was remarkable to observe how quickly fanatical Nazis, taken prisoner, veered round from arrogant superiority to obsequious acceptance of British authority and downright admiration of our way of doing things. In other words, German loyalty to the national group is largely dependent on its successful assertion of power. Germans tend to turn against their own country when its power shows signs of weakening, or when they are under a new authority. This ambivalence and duality which pervades so many Germans of the present day has undoubtedly contributed to giving a paranoid flavour, to put it mildly, to the Nazi movement. Their blatant assertion of national superiority and uniqueness, coupled with the compulsion to see internal and external enemies everywhere, resulting finally in their "justified" acts of aggression and brutality, are clinical facts in evidence of this statement. This paranoid behaviour could be interpreted in terms of psychopathology as being founded on the stifled wish to be the favoured and irresponsible baby, and on the rejection of paternal authority and order which they had so overwhelmingly to accept in their own society. The resultant unconscious frustration rage and its attendant guilt feelings were projected on to the many scapegoat symbols, and led to all the persecution for internal treason and all the heresy hunting, characteristic of the later Nazi period, when external successes waned and the ambivalence towards authority became more marked. There seems little doubt that the clique of leading Nazis were not simply exploiting this national psychological

structure in a cunningly rational way, but that they were
themselves deeply emotionally involved in this paranoid
dynamic. Only in this way can we account for their supreme
misjudgments of reality situations, in such matters as the power
potentials of the free world or the reactions of other nations to
their bullying, which ultimately led them with somnambulistic
sureness to defeat. This lack of insight and perspective is
consistent with the gift for painstaking organisation and
planning of detail, itself a function of the need for order and
exactitude as a defence against the inner anarchy and division
which has been so amply demonstrated in German behaviour
over the last fifteen years, when one clique of Nazi bosses was
plotting against another and the scramble for power was barely
masked by the defiant shouts of solidarity and unity of Goebbels's
propaganda machine.

Lastly it must not be forgotten that even hypochondria is a
fairly well established symptom among the German élite. No
country in the world has so many small and delectable spas
where the insightless, greedy, over-driving Herrenvolk can take
their psychosomatic distresses, their functional "heart and nerve"
disorders, and place them in the hands of the witch doctors
abounding at these places and wash away their guilt in passive
submission to purificatory rituals of countless varieties of
healing waters, nature cures and the regimented ordeal by
fasting.

It is against this cultural background now confidently drawn
by the observations of social scientists and psychiatrists that we
have to appraise Hess's own disease. It may well be asked by
how much his individual behaviour differs in quality or
quantity from that of the Nazi movement as a whole. Speaking
on the basis of large experience with many fanatical high-
ranking Nazi personalities, we can say at once that only very
few—less than one per cent—have shown such involvement of
the total personality in a paranoid system as was the case with
Hess. In the main we can agree with the historian F. Foerster
(*Europe and the German Problem*, page 56) that privately such men
can be charming and cultivated, but that "as soon as the
conversation turns to politics their speech and thought suddenly
breathes an arctic chill . . . these might seem to be victims of a
peculiar disease. Even a man of such high intellectual and

artistic endowments as Frederick the Great gave proof in the sphere of international politics of what was little short of moral insanity. . . . These statesmen live untroubled in this complete contradiction that they deprive the political thought of their people of all higher lights and thereby of any realism which penetrates below the surface". That is to say, their paranoid thinking with its acceptance of political projection, scape-goats, justification of brutality and aggression has not extended right through their personality but has been limited to group affairs. Such prisoners of war made good rapport, accepted without question food and drink and medical aid and took the purely personal intentions of their captors at their face value and placed reliance on them. Their personalities and private lives had not been invaded by their group attitudes, which determined, in however unpleasant a direction, their political conduct only, and their defensive barriers against clinical breakdown held out, even in circumstances of much greater trial and provocation than Hess was ever subjected to, for, unlike them, he received special medical consideration during every moment of his captivity.

It is not exactly known to the authors of this volume to what extent Hess in the early days of the Nazi Party was an active creator of its policies and outlook; that is to say, to what extent his personal paranoid ideas permeated this group. There is some evidence that he imported and incorporated the use of Haushofer's ideas on "geopolitik" and "lebensraum" into the programme. There can be little doubt that he would also have contributed a good deal of the uprooted, unemployed and resentful ex-officer mentality to the movement.

Psychopathology.

It is not wise to make dogmatic statements about the psycho-pathological origins of a given case unless all the con-tributing factors, including the unconscious fantasies, have been subjected to exhaustive study and analysis. Nevertheless, the general experience of psychiatrists in dealing with analogous cases justifies some degree of speculation about the personality which has so greatly intrigued the world by his startling behaviour in 1941.

1. *Constitutional Factors.*

From the point of view of physique and constitution we have seen the presence of a number of so-called stigmata of degeneration. The extremely primitive skull formation, the misshapen ears, the arched, narrow palate and the dental malformation, coupled with asthenic body build and a narrow centrally placed heart, justify the assertion that Hess's physique was dysplastic—a feature which Kretschmer would associate with schizophrenic tendencies.

2. *Mental Heredity.*

Here we note the history of suicide and mental disorder on both sides of the family in the parents siblings. Details are unfortunately not available.

3. *Early Environment.*

We can draw few inferences from the somewhat typical Victorian-German history of a stern father of whom the children were frightened. This is the story of many of us, but it may be significant to note how in later years Hess sought out father-surrogates to "influence" him: the history-master at Godesberg, Haushofer at Munich University and lastly Hitler. Like his father in later years, these two early teachers were rewarded handsomely by Hess when he became successful.

On an occasion of relaxation, he confided to one of us that he had felt antagonistic towards his father in earlier days, though this trait does not appear to have influenced his behaviour, which was that of the good, earnest pupil, obediently following the father's wish to take up a business career against his inclination. This submission to the father is the typical story of many an authoritarian character, as we have been able to show in examining German Nazi personalities. We can infer from our general acquaintance with such people the formation of a considerable *ambivalence*—a split of feelings of love and of antagonism towards the father, of which the hate part is usually repressed. In this situation is the making of an unconscious passive homosexual disposition, which, in turn, is widely held by psychiatrists to play an important part in later paranoid attitudes.

Next we have to refer to the marked sense of identity of interest between Hess and his mother, expressed in his pursuit of nature cure and odd medical and occult studies, which, significantly under the guidance of an old woman fortune-teller, were to become so morbidly prominent. This division of personal allegiance between his two parents is in itself no uncommon feature in the psychological history of human beings. In Hess this split appears to have become unusually marked. We note the antithesis of the street-fighter and the sentimentalist who fishes a wasp out of the jam-pot; the tough mountaineer and the health-faddist; the storm-troop leader and the dog-like devotee and follower.

Many psychological observers are agreed that the German domestic culture favours this sado-masochistic, dominant-submissive cleavage or duality. The inability successfully to resist the father's power, and the feeling of weakness or in-feriority so created, are apt to result in a persistence of adolescent hero-fantasies. At the core of such romanticism lies the primary need to overcome the father and deliver one's mother—a theme upon which countless myths and fairy tales of monsters slain and damsels rescued are founded. It is a commonplace of psychology that among the transformations which such ideas undergo in developing youths, the appeal of the motherland to be delivered from a cruel oppressor is one of the most favoured mechanisms producing patriotic fervour.

It is not surprising to find Hess a militant patriot who welcomed the first World War as an opportunity for casting off, without blame, the humiliating drudgery of the distasteful and un-heroic career imposed on him by his father. Neither are we astonished when we learn of his later fervour in resisting the "un-German" democratic movements—already savouring of "Jewish-Bolshevik" contamination—during the 1918-23 period.

The personal roots of Hess's outstanding sense of inner weakness and contamination can be derived from his un-recognised, repressed passive streak, as it were the mother in him, and from his persistent adolescent auto-erotism. Every psychiatrist will know the reactions which such immaturities are apt to engender in sensitive individuals. Both passivity and masturbation may lead to frantic efforts at ascetic self-control, over-assertion of strength and masculinity and intolerance of weakness, due to the haunting dread of being morally bad and inferior. In this situation we may find the connection between the "healthy life, go-to-the-mountains from whence cometh strength" side, and the morbid preoccupation with his body in Hess's character. A small incident which occurred at Maindiff may be of interest to the psychiatrically-trained reader as an illustration of these trends. Hess had had a nocturnal emission, and at once attributed this to an egg he had eaten the day before. He vowed forthwith to abstain from eggs in the future.

We are brought back to the commonplaces of the immature, self-preoccupied neurotic personality. His relation to his wife— a simple girl of somewhat inferior social status to his own—was typical. She appears to have been kept away from all public and even Party functions and confined to her Germanic domestic sphere on principle, not even sharing his lime-light, but constituting a small adjunct of his private life, in which he was within his limits kindly and considerate. It was the marriage of a self-centred person—and it was very German.

4. *The Role of National Socialism.*

It can be readily seen how well the Nazi movement corre-sponded to the needs of a paranoid mystical fantast like Hess, suffering from the profound feelings of guilt and isolation—the intellectual *manqué*. Here was a movement in which he met many birds of his feather, but was able to satisfy both sides of the polarity of his character, namely, the need to play a certain heroic role with Messianic implications and promise; on the other hand to subordinate himself loyally and passively to a more powerful masculine authority figure. To him, with his personal fantasies of internal contamination, the notion of a contaminated Germany to be cleansed and purified must have made a great appeal. The psychotic notion of division of personality, one part ill and weak and poisoned, which could be joined to the other part incorporating the adolescent hero fantasy, was most likely based on masturbation guilt.* To be able to identify himself with a group which rejected this guilt and attributed it to the mysterious activities of impure, because foreign, elements (Jews, Communists, Vatican, international Freemasonry and all the rest of the paranoid scapegoat galaxy)

---

* We recall here the Parsifal story in which Amfortas the King by his sin has become incurable and the Holy Grail dim, to be saved by the "Pure Fool" Parsifal. The appeal of this theme to Germans, in Wagner's lush rendering, is well-known.

must have been to experience great lightening of guilt, just as externally Hess, with his rather exotic appearance and foreign Levantine antecedents (he was nicknamed "the Egyptian" by his Party friends), must have been gratified to worship the purity of Germanic blood.

It is probable that so long as the Party was functioning on the planning and campaigning level, his idealism and sense of mission and the exhilarating cameraderie of a group of "light bringers" amply fulfilled his needs for significance and extraversion and so kept him well and happy as a central figure of the band of brothers as well as satisfying his needs for fighting and playing the man. His later role would appear to have been a more feminine one of standing faithfully by Hitler's side, dealing with the charitable aspects of the Party, giving Christmas broadcasts to the mothers, hearing appeals and enjoining obedience and loyalty on the people towards their great father leader. We have the evidence of our journalist informant (see Chapter V page 57) for thinking that Hess was not altogether happy in the more gangster-like developments of power politics, which from inner necessity became more marked as Nazi power became securely established, although there is reason to think that he would have sanctioned all measures directed against his personal scapegoats in so far as they were also those of the Nazi programme, i.e., Jews and Communists. It is likely that the brutal actions of the S.S. and the Gestapo must have been known to him and that they must have stimulated his own latent sense of guilt and so led to an exacerbation at any rate of the hypochondriacal aspects of his persecution system. He thereby naturally acquired the reputation of a health-faddist and crank, and became to some extent a figure of ridicule and contempt in his circle, whose self-announced motto was Hitler's "tough as leather, hard as Krupp steel, lithe as a greyhound". Such an old-womanish pastime as visiting nature doctors and consulting the stars was ridiculed even by Hitler, who, we know, privately also had considerable feminine and magical behaviour traits which he would all the more have tried to conceal in public. One can imagine Hess being the ideal foil on to which all the extravagant fads and irrationalities of the Nazi leaders as a whole could be off-loaded. We are probably justified in thinking that at least one motive for his flight to England could have been his growing sense of isolation and waning influence. It is believed that Hitler always disapproved of Hess's wife, who was said to have been at loggerheads with Hitler's now famous last girl-friend, Eva Braun.

5. *Development of Symptoms During Captivity.*

If it is true to say that the paranoid reaction to life is based on pathological self-evaluation, then it can readily be conceded that Hess's fantasy of peace-maker and hero, which we might call the grandiose component of the paranoid system, received an extremely rude shock on landing in Britain. Instead of finding an enthusiastic reception at the hands of England's most exalted society and even at the throne itself, he was treated as a prisoner behind barbed wire and interviewed only on our own terms. Although under the Geneva Convention and by international usage he was given suitably decent conditions, the very surroundings in which he found himself must have enhanced his ambivalence and emphasised his fantasies of conspiracy and suspicion. Looking back, it might be considered to have been a mistake in the psychiatric handling of the case that the house in which he was first confined was divided into two messes; one the "jeunesse dorée" of the young Guards officers to whom all his homosexual attraction went out, and who were representatives of the chivalrous symbol of the King of England, but who had very little contact with him; on the other side were the rather obvious political intelligence officers, representatives to Hess of the melodramatic notions of the British Secret Service writ large, which so many Germans feel to be ubiquitous. These evil figures stood between him and the more attractive young representatives of what he took to be the King's household, and were no doubt, so he felt, in league with the Jewish-Bolshevik conspiracy.

It was interesting that, with every demonstration, whether by act or by logical persuasion, of our good faith, when he had to admit that his persecutory fears were groundless, his internal distress increased. Thus he would have more insomnia, or more abdominal cramp, or more fatigue. Quite apart from this case as such, the interdependence of the mechanisms of introjection and projection in psychopathology were very clearly demonstrated, together with the role which projection plays in the relief of internal guilt tensions.

It is usually held that a classic case of paranoia will, sooner or later, give vent to the accumulating tension of destructive impulses in some act of murder or violence directed against a scapegoat figure. It is interesting, therefore, to remind ourselves that such an attack was actually expected by us, and one of us at the time of the first suicidal attempt on June 16th, 1941, felt fairly certain that he was to be the victim of the attack. It is likely therefore that the suicide which not a few paranoid personalities attempt is an equivalent of such a murderous attack, where the projection has not been completely made and where the enemy is still to some extent felt to be inside one's self, there to be attacked and destroyed. We can understand more easily the attempt at suicide which took place at Maindiff at the time when Germany was manifestly losing the war and Hess's fate was in any case sealed, but to try and commit suicide at a time when Hess and most of the rest of the world were convinced that nothing could prevent Germany from winning the war, and when he himself still dared to be convinced that Hitler would understand his motives and reinstate him in favour when he had won the war, needs a psychopathological comment. Was Hess, in the manner of many psychopathic personalities, intuitively aware that Germany's cause was already lost, or did he act purely impulsively on the impact of internal psychotic self-destructive motives which he failed to project in the manner of a true paranoia on to some figure to kill? Or again, was this a true depressive act of self-punishment, by which he was punishing his ego for failure in comparison with the grandiose hero-fantasy which his ego ideal demanded should be successfully put into practice?

It is because of the incomplete and somewhat unstable nature of his paranoid system and the constant intrusion of other abnormal mechanisms, and indeed sometimes of normal insight, that the case constitutes such an interesting diagnostic problem, quite apart from the general interest of the setting of the case. This is particularly true of the amnesia, which, beginning towards the latter part of 1941, became a complicating feature of his condition. There was no doubt in any of our minds that the first major amnesia (October, 1943 to February, 1945) was genuine in the sense in which a hysterical dissociation can be said to be genuine. Not only was his increasing isolation and indeed loneliness beginning to tell on him, but the war news was taking a turn which demanded some increased defensive system against intolerable reality. The symptom enabled him unconsciously to select whatever sectors of reality he wished to maintain contact with and shut out others, whether memories or present-day events. At the same time it provided a useful handle upon which to hang a request for repatriation, which he used on several occasions. Lastly, and perhaps most importantly from the point of view of mental diagnosis, it undoubtedly provided a mechanism by which his internal tension and suffering could be reduced to a minimum. During the period of his amnesia, we were not surprised therefore that his psychotic paranoid mechanisms became inconspicuous. During an interview which he had at that time with one of us, he was strongly urged to undergo evipan narcosis with a view to undoing the amnesia which he professed to be very distressing to him. He replied that he not only abhorred the idea of foreign substances being injected into his blood stream (a natural enough repugnance in view of his hypochondriacal system) but he said he preferred his state of narrowed consciousness, which would save him a lot of mental suffering, which was good enough for him to maintain a vegetative existence in his prison conditions and which he felt sure would pass away again when he returned home, where he could have the kind of treatment he liked. When eventually we succeeded in persuading him to have evipan, we found him very fully defended and mentally prepared in a manner which has been seen in paranoid, severely narcissistic patients.*

When eventually he came out of his amnesic state and his paranoid systems returned, he pooh-poohed its reality and boasted with considerable malicious pleasure that he had practised a clever piece of deception on the doctors. We note in passing that the date of his recovery of memory coincided roughly with the greatly increased intensity of V-2 attacks on Britain and with German hopes of the success of the Ardennes

---

* Compare Dicks, H. V., Analysis under Hypnotics—Individual Psychology Pamphlets, No. 23, 1944.

offensive. As he made the same claim during the Nuremberg
trials, it may be worth while stating that this boast did not carry
any conviction with us; rather it was to be expected of a person
with his severely disturbed sentiment of self-regard—or to use
the popular phrase, inferiority complex—that, rather than
admit to being a "weak" hysteric, he would have preferred this
explanation which did more credit to his vanity. However, in
letters at that time he expressed relief that his affliction of
memory had passed away.

By and large, therefore, it has been our point of view that, in
common with his cultural pattern and reinforced personal need
to reject weakness and ambivalence in himself, Hess unconsciously has made use of the paranoid projection mechanism
in order to defend himself against his own sense of guilt. It is
possible that he took flight from Germany because the idealised
fantasy relationship towards Hitler as the perfect ideal father
figure had become threatened. We have stressed earlier the
paranoid individual's need to keep in good relations with at
least one person. It may well be that, at Haushofer's mystic
suggestion, he now chose as his new "good figure" the gallant
Duke of Hamilton as a British aristocrat and sportsman and
somehow representative of the King himself, instead of the
tarnished Hitler. Acting on a fantasy, prevalent as has been
mentioned above in even the most fanatical Nazi circles, that
the English responded with similar admiration towards the
Germans, he may have set out literally to seek their protection
from an intolerable predicament in Germany, whilst at the
same time disguising this unconscious need by a peace mission
which, had it been successful, would have restored his need for
being a good and heroic figure. At the same time, in displacing
this ambivalence to what was, after all, the external enemy at
war with Germany, it can be said that he evaded the still
greater conflict of having to betray hostility towards and disagreement with the Nazi movement itself. It looks as if, by
transferring the scene of his psychosis from Germany to England,
he had effected a saving in anxiety tension, and by falling back
upon the cliché so dear to the Nazis of a Bolshevik-Jewish plot
against him in the enemy country he could evade the quite
intolerable feeling that he was being isolated and attacked by a
real plot against him on the part of the S.S., with Hitler not

sufficiently interested to save his prestige and position from being hopelessly undermined.

There are two pieces of confirmatory evidence in support of this hypothesis. The first is the curious persistence in his paranoid ideas of a secret poison which causes a glassy stare in the eyes of its victims. It will be recalled how many of those in attendance on Hess seemed to him to show this eye-change. This may well have been a displacement from Hitler whose "glassy stare" at the frequent moments of fury and hysterical behaviour is notorious. Here indeed was the rationalisation of how good, pure, chivalrous men could be made into criminals and murderers without guilt—for it was all done by Jewish poison.

The second piece of evidence is the statement made by his secretary, who refers to the increasing divorce of her employer from the "bad men" who gained influence in the Nazi hierarchy and against whom he tried to assert himself in vain.

In the long document reproduced in Chapter VIII, we also find Hess projecting temptations to disloyalty on to various British personalities around him, and we are entitled to infer that such temptations might have been present in his own unconscious mind, and dealt with in the paranoid way.

THE DIAGNOSIS

Finally, we must break surface and return to the problem of psychiatric diagnosis. It will have been noticed by the medical reader how carefully the many distinguished psychiatrists and physicians at Nuremberg had avoided tying a diagnostic label to Hess's case, and how justly. The reader may turn back with profit to the *Lancet* article at the beginning of this book and re-read it in the light of its contents.

We note the many points in Hess's history and observed behaviour which would favour the diagnosis of schizophrenia of a paranoid type. Kraepelin in 1896 unified the concept of this disease—then called dementia praecox—and showed the several varieties of clinical forms it might take, from simple dementia to the systematised delusional state of gradual development, without hallucinations, called paranoia. In this series the notion of paraphrenia as an intermediate clinical entity was included. Bleuler further elaborated this systematisation and introduced schizophrenia as the common name.

H

As Macfie Campbell states, these neat technical terms have become shopworn and "degraded currency". There are typical cases for each of Bleuler's categories—but more frequently the individual patient shows an admixture of several of them and cannot be labelled as any one of them. What is beyond question is the presence in Hess of an underlying tendency to thought disorder of the paranoid-schizophrenic type, seen clinically, mirrored in the result of the Rorschach test, and at times admitted by himself.

We drew attention to the episodic rise and fall in this paranoid state, chiefly under the influence of environmental factors, but occasionally not to be interpreted as merely due to these outer circumstances. There is, further, at times a preponderance of hypochondriacal preoccupation which appears to ante-date the persecutory system, and at other times a prevalence of the latter system. Yet at other times both are present in equal degree, justifying the psychopathological interpretation of this form of hypochondriasis as "internalised persecution". Unfortunately we have little evidence on which to say whether his persecution fears were already present before he came under observation. His imprisonment cannot but have aggravated them. One of us (D. M. K.) was more impressed with the hysterical than with the psychotic aspect of Hess's condition. This introduces a considerable complication in terms of descriptive psychiatry. Henderson and Gillespie (3rd edition of their *Textbook of Psychiatry*, page 439) state that hysterical mechanisms occur in schizophrenia and quote an example of aphonia in such a case. In Hess's case the true amnesia of 1943, on which all observers were agreed, almost completely masked the paranoid features, which reappeared in full force when the amnesia was given up, culminating in the hystero-dramatic second attempt at suicide.

We do not think that Hess's paranoid state was so short-lived or situationally determined as to conform to the "formes frustes" described by Gierlich and Friedmann (quoted by D. K. Henderson in *Psychopathic States*, page 106). For this the continuation and gradually widening circle of paranoid thinking was too marked a feature.

Fortunately, the modern point of view in psychiatry is more concerned with the structure and dynamics of the total personality than with attaching diagnostic labels. In this account of Hess as we saw him and as his life story has revealed him, he appears as a self-centred, shy, shut-in, "autistic" personality, submissive but antagonistic to his father in early life, more devoted to his mother and what she stood for, suffering from guilt and an unsettled employment problem, given to an unstable alternation between heroic aggressive and doggedly-industrious, submissive patterns of living, caught in the swirling political currents of his country, with whose fate he becomes emotionally identified and whose extreme forms of irrationalities he is driven to adopt by his craving for devotion and fantasies of glory. He basks briefly but uneasily in the early sunshine of Nazi success but his haunting sense of inadequacy and inner conflict destroy his influence in a position of power far beyond his capacity—perhaps a little to his credit in the setting in which he was expected to live his life.

Coupled with his physical make-up, this story, with its rich variety of morbid symptomatology, with the interchangeability and fluidity of compensatory mechanisms dependent to a great extent on the external circumstances, but without good evidence of deterioration, tempts us to place him in the group of psychopathic personalities of the schizoid type. Hysterical dissociation fits in with this notion of a tendency to splitting in the personality. Kraepelin and Bleuler have shown us the relationship between schizophrenic and paranoid reaction patterns. W. R. D. Fairbairn* has lately pointed to the frequency of the schizoid personality structure in hysterical subjects—a link which Hess's Rorschach response clearly shows.

In this book we have tried, in Adolf Meyer's words, not to sort out the patient but the facts. This we have endeavoured to do faithfully, and we may safely leave the problem of final diagnosis to the predilections and judgments of our colleagues present and future.

* *Endopsychic Structure* Int. J. Psychoanal, XXV, 1944.

APPENDIX

THE actual documents (with verbal corrections made) which were presented to the Court on November 24th are here reproduced. The non-medical reader may wonder at the use of different terms in the various reports. The expert reads the terms in the context of the idioms of psychiatry in the countries of origin.

INTERNATIONAL MILITARY TRIBUNAL

THE UNITED STATES OF AMERICA, THE FRENCH REPUBLIC, THE UNITED KINGDOM OF GREAT BRITAIN & NORTHERN IRELAND, and THE UNION OF SOVIET SOCIALIST REPUBLICS,

—against—

HERMANN WILHELM GÖRING, et al.

Defendants

ORDER

1. Counsel for the defendant Hess has made application to the Tribunal to appoint an expert designated by the medical faculty of the University of Zurich or of Lausanne to examine the defendant Hess with reference to his mental competence and capacity to stand trial. This application is denied.
2. The Tribunal has designated a commission composed of the following members:

Eugene Krasnushkin, M.D., Professor of Psychiatry, Medical Institute of Moscow.

Eugene Sepp, M.D., Professor of Neurology,
Medical Institute of Moscow,
Member, Academy of Medical Sciences, USSR.

Nicolas Kurshakov, M.D., Professor of Medicine,
Medical Institute of Moscow,
Chief Internist, Commissarist of Public Health, USSR.

Lord Moran, M.D., F.R.C.P.,
President of the Royal College of Physicians, London.

Dr. J. R. Rees, M.D., F.R.C.P.,
Medical Director, The Tavistock Clinic, London,
Consulting Psychiatrist to the Army.

Dr. George Riddoch, M.D., F.R.C.P.,
Director of Neurology to the London Hospital,
Consulting Neurologist to the Army.

Dr. Nolan D. C. Lewis, M.D., Professor of Psychiatry,
Columbia University.

Dr. D. Ewen Cameron, M.D., Professor of Psychiatry,
McGill University.

Col. Paul Schroeder, M.D., Neuropsychiatric Consultant,
A.U.S.
University of Illinois.

Dr. Jean Delay, M.D., Professor of Psychiatry at the
Faculty of Medicine, Paris.

The Tribunal has requested the commission to examine the defendant Hess and furnish a report on the mental state of the defendant with particular reference to the question whether he is able to take part in the trial, specifically: (1) Is the defendant able to plead to the indictment? (2) Is the defendant sane or not, and on this last issue the Tribunal wishes to be advised whether the defendant is of sufficient intellect to comprehend the course of the proceedings of the trial so as to make a proper defence, to challenge a witness to whom he might wish to object and to understand the details of the evidence.

3. The examiners have presented their reports to the Tribunal in the form which commends itself to them. It is directed that copies of the reports be furnished to each of the

Chief Prosecutors and to defence counsel. The Tribunal will hear argument by the Prosecution and by defence counsel on the issues presented by the reports on Friday, November 30th at 4 p.m.

INTERNATIONAL MILITARY TRIBUNAL

/s/   Geoffrey Lawrence
Geoffrey Lawrence
President.

Dated Nürnberg, Germany this
24th day of November, 1945.

Copies of four (4) Medical Reports attached.

I.

REPORT on Rudolf Hess, telephoned from London.

"The undersigned, having seen and examined Rudolf Hess, have come to the following conclusion:

1. There are no relevant physical abnormalities.
2. His mental state is of a mixed type. He is an unstable man, and what is technically called a psychopathic personality. The evidence of his illness in the past four years, as presented by one of us who has had him under his care in England, indicates that he has had a delusion of poisoning, and other similar paranoid ideas.

Partly as a reaction to the failure of his mission, these abnormalities got worse, and led to suicidal attempts.

In addition, he has a marked hysterical tendency, which has led to the development of various symptoms, notably a loss of memory, which lasted from November, 1943, to June, 1944, and which resisted all efforts at treatment. A second loss of memory began in February, 1945, and lasted till the present. This amnesic symptom will eventually clear, when circumstances change.

3. At the moment he is not insane in the strict sense. His loss of memory will not entirely interfere with his comprehension of the proceedings, but it will interfere with his ability to make his defence, and to understand details of the past, which arise in evidence.

4. We recommend that further evidence should be obtained by narco-analysis and that if the Court decides to proceed with the Trial, the question should afterwards be reviewed on psychiatric grounds."

(Signed) Moran
J. R. Rees
George Riddoch.

Dated 19th November, 1945.

II.

20th November, 1945.

MEMORANDUM TO: Brigadier-General Wm. L. Mitchell,
General Secretary for the Inter-
national Military Tribunal.

In response to the request of the Tribunal that the defendant Rudolf Hess be examined, the undersigned psychiatrists examined Rudolf Hess on 15th and 19th November, 1945, in his cell in the Military Prison in Nürnberg.

The following examinations were made: physical, neurological and psychological.

In addition, documents were studied bearing information concerning his personal development and career. Reports concerning the period of his stay in England were scrutinised. The results of all psychological, special psychometric examinations and observations carried out by the prison psychiatrist and his staff were studied. Information was also derived from the official interrogation of the defendant on 14th November and 16th November, 1945.

(1) We find, as a result of our examinations and investigations, that Rudolf Hess is suffering from hysteria characterised in part by loss of memory. The nature of this loss of memory is such that it will not interfere with his comprehension of the proceedings, but it will interfere with his response to questions relating to his past and will interfere with his undertaking his defence.

In addition there is a conscious exaggeration of his loss of memory and a tendency to exploit it to protect himself against examination.

(2) We consider that the existing hysterical behaviour which the defendant reveals was initiated as a defence against the circumstances in which he found himself while in England; that it has now become in part habitual and that it will continue as long as he remains under the threat of imminent punishment, even though it may interfere with his undertaking a more normal form of defence.

(3) It is the unanimous conclusion of the undersigned that Rudolf Hess is not insane at the present time in the strict sense of the word.

(s) D. Ewen Cameron
DR. D. EWEN CAMERON
Professor of Psychiatry,
McGill University.

(s) Jean Delay
DR. JEAN DELAY
Professor of Psychiatry at the
Faculty of Medicine in Paris.

(s) Paul L. Schroeder
COL. PAUL L. SCHROEDER
A.U.S. Neuropsychiatric
Consultant.

(s) Nolan D. C. Lewis
DR. NOLAN D. C. LEWIS
Professor of Psychiatry,
Columbia University.

III.

RECORD OF EXAMINATION OF RUDOLF HESS

According to the information obtained on November 16th 1945, during the interrogation of Rosenberg, who had seen Hess immediately before the latter's flight to England, Hess gave no evidence of any abnormality either in appearance or conversation. He was, as usual, quiet and composed. Nor was it apparent that he might have been nervous. Prior to this, he was a calm person, habitually suffering pains in the region of the stomach.

As can be judged on the basis of the report of the English psychiatrist, Doctor Rees, who had Hess under observation from the first days of his flight to England, Hess, after the airplane crash, disclosed no evidence of a brain injury, but upon arrest and incarceration he began to give expression to ideas of persecution, he feared that he would be poisoned or killed, and his death represented as a suicide, and that all this would be done by the English under the hypnotic influence of the Jews. Furthermore, these delusions of persecution were maintained up to the news of the catastrophe suffered by the German Army at Stalingrad, when the manifestations were replaced by amnesia. According to Doctor Rees, the delusions of persecution and the amnesia were observed not to take place simultaneously. Furthermore, there were two attempts at suicide. A knife wound inflicted during the second attempt in the skin near the heart gave evidence of a clearly hystericodemonstrative character. After this there was again observed a change from amnesia to delusions of persecution, and during this period he wrote that he was simulating his amnesia, and finally again entered into a state of amnesia which has been prolonged up to the present.

According to the examination of Rudolf Hess on November 14th, 1945, the following was disclosed.

Hess complains of frequent cramping pains in the region of the stomach which appear independent of the taking of food, and headaches in the frontal lobes during mental strain, and, finally, of loss of memory.

In general his condition is marked by a pallor of the skin and a noticeable reduction in food intake.

Regarding the internal organs of Hess, the pulse is 92, and a weakening of the heart tone is noticeable. There has been no change in the condition of the other internal organs.

Concerning the neurological aspect, there are no symptoms of organic impairment of the nervous system.

Psychologically, Hess is in a state of clear consciousness; knows that he is in prison at Nürnberg under indictment as a war criminal; has read and, according to his own words, is acquainted with the charges against him. He answers questions rapidly and to the point. His speech is coherent, his thoughts formed with precision and correctness and they are accompanied by sufficient emotionally expressive movements. Also, there is no kind of evidence of paralogism. It should also be noted here that the present psychological examination, which was conducted by Lieut. Gilbert, Ph.D., bears out the testimony that the intelligence of Hess is normal and in some instances above the average. His movements are natural and not forced.

He has expressed no delirious fancies, nor does he give any delirious explanation for the painful sensation in his stomach or the loss of memory, as was previously attested to by Doctor Rees, namely, when Hess ascribed them to poisoning. At the present time, to the question about the reason for his painful sensations and the loss of memory, Hess answers that this is for the doctors to know. According to his own assertions, he can remember almost nothing of his former life. The gaps in Hess's memory are ascertained only on the basis of the subjective changing of his testimony about his inability to remember this or that person or event given at different times. What he knows at the present time is, in his own words, what he allegedly learned only recently from the information of those around him and the films which have been shown him.

On November 14th Hess refused the injection of narcotics which were offered for the purpose of making an analysis of his psychological condition. On November 15th, in answer to Professor Delay's offer, he definitely and firmly refused narcosis and explained to him that, in general, he would take all measures to cure his amnesia only upon completion of the trial.

All that has been exposed above, we are convinced, permits of the interpretation that the deviation from the norm in the behaviour of Hess takes the following forms:

i. In the psychological personality of Hess there are no changes typical of the progressive schizophrenic disease, and therefore the delusions from which he suffered periodically while in England cannot be considered as manifestations of a schizophrenic paranoia, and must be recognised as the expression of a psychogenic paranoic reaction, that is, the psychologically comprehensible reaction of an unstable (psychologically) personality to the situation (the failure of his mission, arrest and incarceration). Such an interpretation of the delirious statements of Hess in England is bespoken by their disappearance, appearance and repeated disappearance depending on external circumstances which affected the mental state of Hess.

ii. The loss of memory by Hess is not the result of some kind of mental disease but represents hysterical amnesia, the basis of which is a subconscious inclination toward self-defence as well as a deliberate and conscious tendency toward it. Such behaviour often terminates when the hysterical person is faced with an unavoidable necessity of conducting himself correctly. Therefore, the amnesia of Hess may end upon his being brought to trial.

iii. Rudolf Hess, prior to his flight to England, did not suffer from any kind of insanity, nor is he now suffering from it. At the present time he exhibits hysterical behaviour with signs of a conscious-intentional (simulated) character, which does not exonerate him from his responsibility under the indictment.

Professor Krasnushkin, Doctor of Medicine   (signed)

Professor Sepp, Honorary Scientist, Regular   (signed)
    Member of the Academy of Medicine

Professor Kurshakov, Doctor of Medicine,   (signed)
    Chief Therapeutist of the Commissariat of Health
                    of the U.S.S.R.

17th November, 1945.

TO THE INTERNATIONAL MILITARY TRIBUNAL

In pursuance of the assignment by the Tribunal, we, the medical experts of the Soviet Delegation, together with the physicians of the English Delegation and in the presence of one representative of the American Medical Delegation, have examined Rudolf Hess and made a report on our examination of Mr. Hess together with our conclusions and interpretation of the behaviour of Mr. Hess.

The statement of the general conclusions has been signed only by the physicians of the Soviet Delegation and by Professor Delay, the medical expert of the French Delegation.

    Appendix: (1) Conclusions and (2) the Report on the
              examination of Mr. Hess.

Professor Krasnushkin, Doctor of Medicine   (signed)

Professor Sepp, Honorary Scientist, Regular   (signed)
    Member of the Academy of Medicine

Professor Kurshakov, Doctor of Medicine, Chief   (signed)
    Therapeutist of the Commissariat of Health
    of the U.S.S.R.

17th November, 1945.

IV.

After observation and an examination of Rudolf Hess the undersigned have reached the following conclusions:

1. No essential physical deviations from normality were observed.

2. His mental conditions are of a mixed type. He is an unstable person, which in technical terms is called a psychopathic personality. The data concerning his illness during the period of the last four years, submitted by one of us who had him under observation in England, showed that he had a delusion of being poisoned and other similar paranoic notions.

Partly as a reaction to the failure of his mission there, the abnormal manifestations increased and led to attempts at suicide. In addition to the above mentioned he has noticeable hysterical tendencies which caused a development of various symptoms, primarily, of amnesia that lasted from November, 1943, to June of 1944 and resisted all attempts to be cured.

The amnesia symptom may disappear with changing circumstances.

The second period of amnesia started in February of 1945 and has lasted up through the present.

3. At present he is not insane in the strict sense of the word. His amnesia does not prevent him completely from understanding what is going on around him but it will interfere with his ability to conduct his defence and to understand details of the past which would appear as factual data.

4. To clarify the situation we recommend that a narco-analysis be performed on him and, if the Court decides to submit him to trial, the problem should be subsequently re-examined again from a psychiatric point of view.

The conclusion reached on November 14th by the physicians of the British Delegation, Lord Moran, Dr. J. R. Rees, and Dr. G. Riddoch, and the physicians of the Soviet Delegation, Professors Krasnushkin, Sepp and Kurshakov, was also arrived at on November 15th by the representative of the French Delegation, Professor Jean Delay.

After an examination of Mr. Hess which took place on November 15th, 1945, the undersigned Professors and experts of the Soviet Delegation, Krasnushkin, Sepp and Kurshakov, and Professor Jean Delay, the expert from the French Delegation, have agreed on the following statement:

Mr. Hess categorically refused to be submitted to narco-analysis and resisted all other procedures intended to effect a cure of his amnesia, and stated that he would agree to undergo treatment only after the trial. The behaviour of Mr. Hess makes it impossible to apply the methods suggested in Paragraph 4 of the report of November 14th and to follow the suggestion of that Paragraph in present form.

Professor Krasnushkin, Doctor of Medicine	(Signed)
Professor Sepp, Honorary Scientist, Regular Member of the Academy of Medicine	(Signed)
Professor Kurshakov, Doctor of Medicine, Chief Therapeutist of the Commissariat of Health of The U.S.S.R.	(Signed)
Professor Jean Delay of the School of Medicine In Paris.	(Signed)

16th November, 1945.